THE
ANDY CRANE
MULTI-MEDIA
QUIZ BOOK

Also by Andy Crane:

ANDY CRANE ON TV

With thanks to Nigel Robinson

THE
ANDY CRANE
MULTI-MEDIA
QUIZ BOOK

BANTAM BOOKS
TORONTO · NEW YORK · LONDON · SYDNEY · AUCKLAND

THE ANDY CRANE MULTI-MEDIA BOOK

A BANTAM BOOK   0 553 4005 41

First Publication in Great Britain

PRINTING HISTORY
Bantam Edition published 1991

This book is set in 10pt Times by
Kestrel Data, Exeter

Bantam Books are published by Transworld Publishers Ltd.,
61-63 Uxbridge Road, Ealing, London W5 5SA, in Australia by
Transworld Publishers (Australia) Pty. Ltd., 15-23 Helles Avenue,
Moorebank, NSW 2170, and in New Zealand by Transworld Publishers
(N.Z.) Ltd., Cnr. Moselle and Waipareira Avenues, Henderson, Auckland.

Made and printed in Great Britain by
Cox & Wyman Ltd., Reading, Berks.

CONTENTS

INTRODUCTION

Please don't treat this as just another quiz book – because that's not what it's there for. If you don't know the answers it's the easiest thing in the world simply to flick to the back and find the answers. After all, any nana can do that. I even thought of printing two books – one with the answers and one with the questions.

Why not do a Sherlock Holmes and try and track down the answers yourself? That's what TV researchers do every day to bring you your favourite programmes!

Some of the questions in this book are admittedly more difficult or more obscure than the others – but there isn't a single one which can't be answered with a couple of minutes thought and application. And the satisfaction you'll get at not taking the easy way out will certainly make up for the time and work you spend discovering the answers.

The first place to start, of course, is your school or local reference library. Libraries are free and open to everyone and you don't have to limit yourself just to the children's part of the library.

Every library is divided into individual areas for different groups of subjects. For instance there will be an area for scientific and technological subjects, an area for music (both classical and pop), an area for biographies. Each library will also have an index system which will list every book in the library and tell you where that book is – all you need to know is the author's name and the title – you don't need to know the publisher. Of course the librarians can also help you find whatever book you want; don't be afraid to ask for their assistance – after all that's what they're there for!

The one largest source of information in a library will come from the encyclopaedias which every library stocks. The mega-encyclopaedia, of course, is the *Encyclopaedia Britannica* but if you do use that make sure that it's an up-to-date edition. A good modern encyclopaedia is the *Hutchinson Concise Encyclopaedia*, and the *Pears Cyclopaedia* and *Junior Cyclopaedia* are sort of mini-encyclopaedias arranged by subject – in them you'll find sections on science, books, mythology, famous people, plus maps of all the countries of the world. In addition there are lots of 'junior' encyclopaedias which are just as good – ask your teacher or librarian which one they recommend.

There are also lots of other sources of general reference in your library. One especially fun one is *The Guinness Book of Records* and is published annually; like *Recordbreakers* on TV it tells you what's the biggest, the best, the smallest and the worst in any area you care to name. So if you want to find out which pop record has sold the greatest ever number of copies or which movie lost the most money, that's the place to go.

For more specific information go to the part of the library devoted to that subject: in the science section, for instance, you will be able to find scientific dictionaries and manuals which tell you, for instance, just how your television set works; in the music section will be books on both your favourite pop stars and classical composers.

If you find yourself getting more involved in the subject you're researching your local library will also stock a list of special interest groups in your area. Just ask at the desk.

Now, I do realize that some of you out there are going to want to take the easy way out! If you want to look at the answers at the back of the book, fine, but when you've done that why not have a go at making up some questions of your own from the additional information I've provided? And then try your own questions out on your friends – and see just how much they really do know! You could even make up teams and test your knowledge on each other!

I hope you'll learn something from this book. But above all else I hope you have great fun doing it!

SO YOU THINK YOU KNOW ABOUT TV

?

TELEVISUAL TEASERS / 1

In the 1920s a young Scotsman named John Logie Baird started looking into the possibilities of 'seeing by wireless' – or television as it soon came to be known. When he demonstrated his invention no-one really thought it would last: after all there was already radio and if people wanted to see things move they could always go to the cinema and watch films on a wide screen. Who would want to sit at home in front of a tiny box which displayed a hazy flickering picture?

Today, less than seventy years later, television is the most influential medium in the world, and for most people it is their main form of entertainment and means of information. It's our window on the world and brings into our homes the great moments of history – the landing of the men on the Moon, or even England winning the World Cup! We can hear great men and women discuss current events, or see famous works of art in places we might never be able to visit. Television commercials show us what is available in the shops, while consumer programmes like That's Life! *tell us just how good those products are. We can pass the time away watching our favourite rock and classical performers, or relive some of our favourite films. Or we can simply catch up on the comings and goings in Brookside Close or René's Café.*

In Great Britain today 98% of all households have a TV set and the average Briton watches about twenty-one hours of television a week.

And they all said it wouldn't last . . .

Most of the following questions are about TV programmes which are on TV at the moment or have been in the recent past. If you're stuck for an answer, instead of turning to the back for the answers why not just take a look through the pages of your TV listings magazine – there's a good chance the answer will be in there! If you're interested in the history of television programmes and perhaps want to see what your parents were watching at your age, see if your local library has a copy of Box of Delights *by Hilary Kingsley and Geoff Tibballs – it's a year by year guide to TV with lots of fascinating information and gossip!*

1. How many *Blue Peter* badges are there? For which achievement does a viewer receive each of the badges?

2. It's got a pub called the Rover's Return, a corner shop called Alf's Mini-Market and a newsagent's called The Kabin. What is it? (And do you know who runs each of these businesses?)

3. Roy Castle presents which popular TV series based on the bestselling *Guinness Book of Records*?

4. According to the full title of the programme, what are the presenters of *Why Don't You . . . ?* advising you to do?

5. In which TV gameshow would you expect to win a chequebook and pen – if you were unlucky?

6. Which TV presenter, a friend of a more famous gopher, quizzes viewers on the movies?

7. On which programme would you expect to show off the abilities of your talented pet?

8. He's perhaps more famous for travelling through space and time, but he may also ask you 'What's your story?' Who is he?

9. It may stop at the Playground Stop, the Dot Stop, or the Patch Stop. What is it?

10. Which waiter's incompetence was explained by the fact that he was from Barcelona?

11. Which popular TV series are set in:
(a) Walford
(b) Ramsey Street
(c) Weatherfield

12. In which street would you expect to meet Big Bird, and perhaps even Kermit the Frog?

13. Why was Paddington Bear called by this name?

14. Geoffrey, Zippy, George and . . . Who's the missing one in the *Rainbow* team?

15. She started off on a treasure hunt and ended up asking you to challenge her. Who is she?

16. British TV's most successful music programme ever has been seen on TV every week since 1 January 1964. What is it?

17. And which disc jockey, now better known for fixing it, was its very first presenter?

18. On 9.25 on Saturday you might hitch a ride on the *Ghost Train*. But where does the 8.15 come from every Saturday?

19. What would you expect Selina Scott and Jeff Banks to be particularly interested in?

20. Which BBC programme regularly invites viewers to ring in to comment about the previous night's television?

Answers on page 117

COMEDY CLASSICS / 1

1. What's the name of Keith Harris' more famous partner who helps him present the *Quack Chat Show*?

2. In *The Last of the Summer Wine* which item of Nora Batty's clothing does Compo particularly like?

3. His wife is called Betty, his daughter's called Jessica, he often wears an old overcoat and a beret, and he is incredibly accident prone. Who is he?

4. Ever since Sir Arthur Conan Doyle wrote the first Sherlock Holmes story in 1891 Holmes has been the most famous detective ever. But which TV superstar, even more famous than the great man himself, played the part of the Rodent Sherlock Holmes?

5. If you went to Spatz, what would you be expected to buy there?

6. Who was 'to the Manor born'?

7. She's a Dame, has a son called Kenny and a daughter called Valmay. She used to be married to Norm and she comes from Moony Ponds, Australia. Who is she?

8. Think you're so smart? Then what was the name of her bridesmaid who is now her constant companion?

9. He's quite possibly the most famous duck in the world and his greatest ambition is to become a presenter on his favourite TV show, *Blue Peter*. Who is he?

10. Who is T-Bag?

11. Name the Two Ronnies.

12. Can you supply the missing partner in these famous TV team-ups?
    (a) ——————— and Mindy
    (b) ——————— and Wise
    (c) ——————— and Ball
    (d) ——————— and Saunders

13. Which fox tells terrible jokes, often followed with the excruciating punchline 'Boom Boom!'?

14. Who might call you a 'right plonker'?

15. What is the Red Dwarf?

16. They live in a lighthouse on a rock. Who are they?

17. What's the name of Scooby Doo's little nephew?

18. Jim London is a Cockney chauffeur in the series *Home, James*. Which famous comedian plays the part of Jim?

19. Basil, Sybil and Manuel all work at which infamous hotel in Torquay?

20. In *The Hitch-Hiker's Guide to the Galaxy* what did Ford Prefect, Arthur Dent, Zaphoid Beeblebrox and Trilian find at the End of the Universe?

Answers on page 119

ADVENTURES IN SPACE

1. He's got two hearts and is approximately 934 years old. He also has a particularly unusual method of travelling through time and space. Who is he?

2. Name two Defenders of the Earth.

3. Simon Cashmere is the lookalike of which teenager from the twenty-third century?

4. Who are the two most famous droids in the TV series *Droids*?

5. Name two of the five Terrahawks.

6. Do you also know the names of their archenemy, and her son?

7. Which actor would take a Highway to Heaven?

8. Why is it advisable never to annoy David Banner?

9. Which famous puppet was driven around by her chauffeur, Parker, in a pink Rolls Royce which carried the registration number FAB 1?

10. Name three of the regular members of the crew of the USS *Enterprise* in *Star Trek*.

11. And name two of the regular members of the crew of the *Red Dwarf*.

12. Clark Kent was a student at Smallville High School. By what name is he better known?

13. In which TV series would you expect to meet Captain Jean-Luc Picard?

14. Name the female member of the Stingray crew.

15. What disaster occurred on the Moon in the year 1999 in the Gerry Anderson series *Space 1999*?

Answers on page 121

SOAP SUDS / 1

Without a doubt soap operas are the most popular form of television drama today. A soap is a long-running series which concerns itself with the daily trials and tribulations of a large cast of regular characters. So great is public interest in the stories that the soaps often make national headlines. Two episodes of EastEnders *broadcast at Christmas were actually watched by over 30 million people, and it's not unusual for a soap to have a regular audience of 15 million or more.*

Soap operas get their name from the early fifties when soap powder companies in the USA sponsored this kind of programme. If you don't know all the answers to these questions it's a good bet that your friends do! The TV listings magazines might help you too, and there are many books published about the more popular soaps.

1. In which state do most of the Ewings live?

2. And in which city do most of the Carringtons live?

3. What's the name of the Manchester district in which *Coronation Street* is set?

4. *EastEnders* takes place in London E8. By what name is this district better known?

5. And where do the stars of *Home And Away* live?

6. How did Scott and Charlene Robinson first meet?

7. When Charlene left Ramsey Street to which Australian city did she go?

8. Name Ken Barlow's adopted daughter.

9. Which visitor to Albert Square tried to kill his own mother in 1990? And why?

10. Who was Blake Carrington married to before he met Krystle?

11. What was the name of the short-lived series which was a spin-off of *Dynasty*?

12. Who fell over a balcony in the very last episode of *Dynasty*?

13. Who had served a short prison sentence for theft before he moved into Ramsey Street?

14. Name Sharon and Bronwyn's aunt in *Neighbours*.

15. The bust of which British monarch who reigned from 1837 to 1901 is to be seen behind the bar in the Queen Vic?

16. Who helps Alf and Audrey behind the counter of Alf's MiniMarket?

17. Can you name the famous soap opera which finished in 1988 after 24 years on television and which centred around the comings and goings of a motel in the Midlands?

18. Name Charlene Robinson's mother.

Answers on page 123

TELEVISUAL TEASERS / 2

1. Can you match up the following quizmasters with the quiz shows they present?
   (a) Bob Holdness   *Blankety Blank*
   (b) Michael Parkinson   *Going For Gold*
   (c) Henry Kelly   *Blockbusters*
   (d) Les Dawson   *Give Us A Clue*

2. He first played this game in 1971, and now, almost a generation later, is playing it again, after having played his cards right. Who is he and what's the name of his game?

3. Can you identify the following families and the series in which they appear from the names which appear below?
   (a) Bradley, Lady Patience, Austin and Charlotte
   (b) Joey, Adrian, and Billy
   (c) Annie, Jack, Joe and Kate
   (d) Liz, Jim, Steve and Andy
   (e) Miss Ellie, JR and Bobby

4. Who quizzes telly addicts?

5. Which TV quiz show is based on the viewer's general knowledge and skill at the game of darts?

6. What might Cilla Black, Bob Carolgees and Gordon

Burns say to an unsuspecting guest on their
television programme?

7. Over twenty years ago a small lugubrious comedian
appeared on a talent show called *Opportunity
Knocks*. Now he's presenting it. Who is he?

8. Which TV quizmaster would ask you a *Question of
Sport*?

9. What are the names of the following TV dogs:
   (a) He's Bernie Winters' best friend
   (b) He was named after the late husband of his
       owner, Ethel Skinner
   (c) He was Doctor Who's computerized assistant and
       the Time Lord's second best friend

10. Neil Buchanan and Tony Gregory have both been
presenters on which Saturday morning ITV
programme?

11. Lulu, Buck's Fizz and even Cliff Richard have all
appeared on this annual contest between the
countries of Europe. Cliff Richard has even appeared
on it twice. What's the name of the competition?

12. Napoleon Solo and Ilya Kuryakin are members of
which top-secret organization?

13. If she's not saying 'That's Life!' she is out looking
for Hearts of Gold. Who is she?

14. Name the Channel Four science programme
presented by ex-*Blue Peter* presenter Caron Keating.
And do you know whose daughter Caron is?

15. *Blankety Blank* is one of the most popular game
shows on British television. Which Irish TV star first
presented it?

16. What would you expect to find on *The Really Wild Show*?

17. In *The Magic Roundabout*, the British version of which was presented by Eric Thompson, Florence was the little girl who would always get into interesting adventures. But what were the names of the dog and the cow?

18. And who would, without fail, remind all the characters when it was 'time for bed'?

19. *Def 2* is the name of the BBC 2 series of programmes especially aimed at the teenage group. Why is it called *Def 2*?

20. Who is always reminding people that he's started so he'll finish?

Answers on page 124

CARTOON CAPERS / 1

1. This cartoon sailor gains amazing strength whenever he eats a certain kind of canned vegetable. Who is the sailor, and what's his favourite food?

2. And do you know the name of his girlfriend?

3. Shaggy's best friend is a dog who has a habit of getting himself involved in some very weird and spooky adventures. Who is he?

4. Wily Coyote is always chasing this animal, and never catching him. Who is he?

5. Who are the constant companions of the following cartoon characters?
   (a) Bullwinkle
   (b) Yogi Bear
   (c) Fred Flintstone
   (d) Mickey Mouse

6. Huey, Dewey and Louie are the nephews of which cartoon character?

7. The COPS are a very special breed of crimefighters in the futuristic Empire City. What do the initials C.O.P.S. stand for?

8. Name two of the Teenage Mutant Hero Turtles.

9. What kind of Peas are Sweet-Pea, Hop-Pea, and Pop-Pea?

10. Who lives in Lost Wood?

11. Skeletor is the archenemy of who?

12. This rabbit includes among his acquaintances Daffy Duck and Elmer Fudd. What's his name?

13. What's the name of Charlie Brown's dog?

14. He's a Belgian boy reporter, has a dog called Snowy, and his friends include Captain Haddock and the Thompson Twins. Who is he?

15. They live on Wimbledon Common and spend most of their time clearing up litter. Who are they, and what's the name of their Great Uncle?

Answers on page 126

BEHIND THE SCENES ON TV / 1

A typical British TV picture is made up of a picture containing about 211,000 dots which are arranged in a sequence of lines. An electron beam scans this picture, reading it like a book, left to right, top to bottom. The beam is then transformed into electrical impulses which are broadcast by large transmitters into your home, where a similar electronic eye in your television set rebuilds the picture from the impulses into the image you see on your screen.

However, not all things on TV are as complicated as that – no matter what some people might have you believe! See how well you know about what goes on on the other side of the TV screen . . .

My Book Andy Crane on TV *will tell you a lot about what goes on in television, and any good encyclopaedia can explain the basic mechanics of television production. The BBC book* On Camera *by Harris Watts is really written for those people already working in television, but is worth a dip in – there's lots of useful technical information there. If you're interested in working in television the BBC produces many useful leaflets on what the different jobs in TV involve – if your local library doesn't have them your schools careers library should. Even the listings magazines like the* Radio *and* TV Times *often carry useful articles about television behind the scenes. The book* Bluff Your Way In Television *by Richard Spence and Victor Van Amerongen is a funny and cynical book about TV, but you might find some useful information in that. An excellent booklet which you may be able to find in your reference library is the* Open Air A-Z of Television *published by the BBC. And finally many of the national newspapers like* The Guardian *or* The Indy *carry interesting articles on television and the way it is managed and produced today.*

1. What do the initials BBC stand for?

2. Do you know when the BBC first started broadcasting a regular television service?

3. What do Granada TV, Central TV, Yorkshire TV, and Thames TV have in common?

4. The weekday morning programme on BBC1, running from approximately 7 a.m. to 9 a.m., is called *Breakfast Time*. The early morning programme on Channel Four is called *The Channel Four Daily*. What's the name of the early morning programme on the third channel, ITV?

5. What is the Licence Fee?

6. The Open University started in 1969. What is the Open University?

7. On 29 July 1981 750 million people throughout the world watched this event as it was broadcast live on TV. What was it?

8. But in 1985 this record was beaten when 1.6 billion people watched which series of charity pop concerts?

9. What is the name of the British pop music award ceremony which is broadcast every year?

10. Until 1989 it could be heard on television but never seen. Now, if you really want to, you can watch it every weekday on TV, either on special programmes or on the news. What is it?

11. At the time of writing Michael Checkland is the Director General of the BBC. What is the job of the Director General?

12. ITV is made up of several different companies, each of which makes programmes for a particular geographical area, such as the North-West of England, as well as programmes which are shown throughout the country (or 'networked' in TV jargon!) Can you name three of the ITV channels?

13. ITV is largely funded by advertisers who pay for time in which to show their commercials. Do you know which sort of products the following famous TV advertisements were promoting?
   (a) Pop star and model Nick Kamen stripped off down to his boxer shorts in a launderette
   (b) Maureen Lipman played a fussy mother called Beattie who had a son called Malcolm
   (c) A man dressed all in black scales mountains, swims rivers, and does daring deeds to give his girlfriend this gift
   (d) A group of chimpanzees, dressed in human clothes, go about the everyday activities of the day like shifting pianos or cleaning the house

14. The landing of the first men on the Moon was seen live by millions of viewers, all over the world. The Moon Landing took place on 21 July in which year?

15. It started on 2 November 1936, and closed down three years later on 1 September 1939. What was it and why did it close down?

Answers on page 128

COMEDY CLASSICS / 2

1. Where would you expect James, Siegfried and Tristram to work? And do you also know the name of the author of the books on which the popular TV series is based?

2. Which family could quite fairly be described as being 'Round The Twist'?

3. Peggy Ollrenshaw's greatest wish was to become a Yellowcoat in the series *Hi De Hi*. Did she ever achieve her ambition and, if so, when?

4. Where would you go if you wanted to inspect that great work of art, *The Fallen Madonna with the Big Boobies*?

5. Name the sergeant of Privates Doberman and Paparelli.

6. Who was the leader of a gang of alleycats, and the chief rival of Officer Dibble?

7. It's been described as a 'situation tragedy' and was set in the Dark Ages. Over the years we've followed the fortunes of the leading character's descendants in a number of other tragic situations. What's the name of this situation comedy?

8. Name three of Mrs Boswell's children.

9. During the 1940s, groups of men, ineligible for entry into the regular army, set up small forces of part-time soldiers ready to do battle in the event of England being invaded. These groups were known as the Home Guard, and were officially encouraged by the Government. One such group was based at Walmington-on-Sea in this classic comedy series, still popular after it was first shown in 1968 (!). What was the name of this series, and can you name three of the regular members of Walmington's home guard?

10. M*A*S*H was one of the most popular American comedy series of all time, and followed the exploits of a group of American soldiers in the Korean War of the 1950s. M*A*S*H is an abbreviation for what?

11. Christopher Reeve might play the role of Superman in the cinema, but even he would have a hard time fighting his TV counterpart Blunderman. Who plays Blunderman on TV?

12. Popular TV sit-coms take place in a wide variety of locations. Which series have taken place in:
(a) a holiday camp
(b) a hamburger joint
(c) a French café, during the German occupation of France in the 1940s

13. Who does Mrs Boswell consider to be a tart?

14. They live in a spooky old house and their first names are Hermann, Lily, Eddie, Marilyn and Granpa. Who are they?

15. Adelaide, Sidney and Bruce the Spider all come

from which country? And what is the name of their touring van?

16. Miami is not known only for its Vice. Blanche, Dorothy, Rose and Sofia all live there too – in which American TV series?

17. Fletcher, played by Ronnie Barker, was imprisoned in Slade Prison in which television series?

18. And which two Birds of a Feather have husbands in prison?

19. If you were found to be wearing a red nose on a certain day of the year which charity could you be reasonably expected of supporting?

20. Name the two married couples in *The Good Life*.

Answers on page 133

SOAP SUDS / 2

1. Of all the members of the current cast of *Coronation Street* only one was seen in the very first episode in 1960. Who was he?

2. Name three of Blake Carrington's children.

3. Which member of the Carrington family was kidnapped by aliens in a flying saucer?

4. In *Neighbours* Jane very nearly got married to an American businessman. How did she meet him?

5. Name Sheila Grant's youngest son. How did he die?

6. In *Coronation Street* shopkeeper Alf is married to Audrey. In *Home And Away* who is shopkeeper Alf married to?

7. Actor Darius Perkins originally played which popular character in *Neighbours*? Which actor replaced Darius in the role?

8. Bobby Ewing died and was buried in 1987. How did he come back from the dead?

9. Who did Sharon give away to the police in *Neighbours*?

10. How was Brian Tilsley, Gail's husband, killed?

11. For whom did Ken Barlow leave his wife Deirdre?

12. Name Bobby Simpson's husband.

13. The members of which soap might drink in The Waterhole?

14. Why did Mrs Mangel leave Ramsey Street in 1990?

15. Down which street has Phyllis Pearce been chasing Percy Sugden for many years now?

16. What's Charlene Robinson's nickname?

17. Who shot J. R. Ewing in 1981?

18. Name the actor who plays Henry in *Neighbours*. What's the name of the pop group he plays in?

Answers on page 135

WHO'S WHO?

Can you recognize all the following TV personalities from their brief descriptions?

1. She might stop you in the street and ask you about your pet's special talents.

2. This former newsreader might ask you to come dancing.

3. While this newsreader is quite likely to arrange for you to be marooned on a desert island with some of your favourite records.

4. These two New Zealanders will show you how to cook your favourite meals – when they stop bickering amongst themselves!

5. She used to play the part of a lady undertaker but now this Lancashire actress may introduce your favourite hymns.

6. This Welsh ex-Goon may find himself on a Highway every Sunday.

7. She's wide awake even when in the company of the Hit Man.

8. She used to take us on a Newsround. Now she's more likely to give us a Grandstand view.

9. Are this outrageous entertainer and his wonderdog the most important members of Joan Collins' fan club?

10. When Jeremy's about you had better watch out!

Answers on page 137

LAW AND ORDER

1. Agatha Christie wrote over eighty detective novels, and is the most successful writer of crime fiction ever. Her two most famous creations have been a monocled, mustachioed Belgian detective, and a mild-mannered English spinster. Each has featured in their own television show. Who are they?

2. At which police station does Juliet Bravo work?

3. What does Jessica Fletcher write?

4. Name the owner of the Moonlighting Detective Agency. Who is her more troublesome partner?

5. Each member of the A-Team was, to say the least, eccentric. But which of them delighted in wearing fancy dress in every episode?

6. William Shatner would once ask Scotty to beam him up. Now he's much more likely to be chasing the villains in a police squad car in which TV cops series?

7. In *Beauty and the Beast* why is Vincent forced to live beneath the streets of New York?

8. By what name are Chicago cops Mary Beth and Chris better known?

9. This incompetent French police inspector was most often seen in the cinema, hunting a beautiful precious stone called The Pink Panther. But he was also seen in a cartoon series with the Pink Panther himself. Who is he?

10. Where would you be advised to 'be careful out there'?

11. Who was searching for the murderer of Daisy in the comedy series *Brass*?

12. Inspector Abberline was a real-life detective who unsuccessfully tried to uncover the identity of Jack the Ripper. One hundred years after Jack the Ripper's murder which famous film actor portrayed Inspector Abberline on television?

13. In *Miami Vice* Paul Michael Thomas and Don Johnson play cool cops Tubbs and Crockett. But who plays the part of Crockett's wife? And for what is she more famous?

14. Where would you expect to find lifeguard Mitch?

15. Which TV detective's work takes him to both Jersey and France?

16. Actor John Thaw plays the part of which music-loving detective?

17. Mrs Emma Peel, Tara King and Purdey have all been the assistants of secret agent John Steed in which cult TV adventure show?

18. Where would you expect to find Horace Rumpole?

19. *The Bill* tells the story of which local police station?

20. Which famous character actor plays Campion's assistant?

Answers on page 138

CARTOON CAPERS / 2

1. Eric is just a normal boy. But when trouble threatens he can transform himself into which all-powerful superhero?

2. Name the pirate captain who sailed the high seas on the ship *The Black Pig* in the company of Tom the cabin boy.

3. Who is the bungling French detective who gets into the most amazing trouble, and whose name is often associated with the Pink Panther?

4. His colleagues are Leekman, Haggisman and Pink Bucket man. Who is he?

5. What's the favourite food of the Teenage Mutant Hero Turtles?

6. What sort of creature is Heathcliff?

7. Which famous TV presenter narrates the story of Stoppit and Tidyup?

8. Who was the cat Sylvester's arch enemy? And who was Tom's enemy?

9. What are the better-known surnames of Stan and Ollie?

10. Your wife is Betty, your son is Bam-Bam and you live in Bedrock. Who are you?

11. Which superhero team is made up of Flash Gordon, Mandrake the Magician and the Phantom?

12. And what's the name of their arch enemy?

13. Who does Lucy Van Pelt have a crush on in the *Peanuts* TV series?

14. 'In the lands of the north where the black rocks stand guard against the cold sea' is the land of Nog. Who was the ruler of that land whose adventures were first seen on television over twenty years ago and can now be seen on video?

15. What sort of animal is Pepe le Pugh?

Answers on page 140

TELEVISUAL TEASERS / 3

1. Which bar or pub do the following people run?
   (a) Rebecca Howe
   (b) Simon Wicks and Sharon Watts
   (c) Alec and Bet Gilroy
   (d) Amos Brierley

2. He's asked you if you were game for a laugh. Now he's telling you that you've been framed! Who is he?

3. Who's been fixing it for people since 1975?

4. Scott Robinson hasn't done it yet, but both Robert Robinson and Anne Robinson have presented this popular 10-minute BBC TV programme. What is it?

5. Name the fitness expert on TV AM.

6. Which former British Prime Minister has been seen to advertise British cheeses on television?

7. Who returned to Coronation Street for one day in 1990 as part of a charity telethon?

8. This chat show host might very well be your Last Resort. Who is he?

9. Can you match up the following characters with the TV series in which they appear?

(a) Detective Inspector
    Burnside   *Porridge*
(b) Bruce Wayne   *Murder, She Wrote*
(c) Stavros   *The Bill*
(d) Sonny Crockett   *Batman*
(e) Norman Stanley
    Fletcher   *Kojak*
(f) Jessica Fletcher   *Miami Vice*

10. Name the fast-talking French presenter of the cult music programme *Rapido*.

11. In the 1960s she was a famous Liverpudlian pop star who sang songs such as *Step Inside Love* and *You're My World*. Who is she and for what is she much better known today?

12. Who came from the planet Ork?

13. What does a 'friendly wave each morning' do?

14. Which Permanent Secretary of State started saying *Yes, Minister* and now says *Yes, Prime Minister*?

15. Which of the following is not an enemy of Doctor Who?
Cybermen; Daleks; Suilurians; Romulans; Urbankans.

Answers on page 142

SOAP SUDS / 3

1. Which character in *EastEnders* reads tealeaves?

2. Who was Pete Beale married to before he met and married Kathy?

3. Which of the following do *not* live in Coronation Street?
   Alec and Bet; Mavis and Derek; Kevin and Sally; Alf and Audrey.

4. Who are John Ross Ewing's mother and father?

5. How much did Helen inherit from Jim's mother in *Neighbours*?

6. How did Miss Ellie's first husband die?

7. Name the youngest son of Jim and Ruth Robinson.

8. After her first husband's death who did Miss Ellie marry?

9. What is Charlene's job?

10. Whose dog is called Little Willie?

11. And whose dog is called Bouncer?

12. In which Australian town is Ramsey Street?

13. Which member of the Ewing family was once a Man From Atlantis?

14. Name the long-established doctor who works in Albert Square.

15. In *Neighbours* who in Poppy's garden needed a nose job, and why?

16. Who bought Hilda Ogden's old house when she left Coronation Street and went to live and work in Derbyshire?

17. Kate O'Mara played the role of Alexis' sister in *Dynasty*. What was her name?

18. Which of the following has Alexis in *Dynasty* never been married to?
Blake Carrington
Cecil Colby
Sean Rowan
Zach Powers
Dex Dexter

Answers on page 143

SOAP SUDS / 4

1. How did Den Watts die?

2. Name the Carringtons' faithful cook.

3. For which newspaper did Scott Robinson work?

4. Can you match up the following married couples who have appeared in *Coronation Street*?
   (a) Kevin   Mavis
   (b) Des   Bet
   (c) Derek   Vera
   (d) Alf   Steph
   (e) Jack   Audrey
   (f) Alec   Sally

5. Who runs the café in *EastEnders*?

6. What is Mrs Mangel's Christian name?

7. Pauline Fowler and Pete Beale have a brother who lives in New Zealand. What's his name?

8. Name Jack and Vera's only son. What's the name of their lodger?

9. And what's the name of Emily Bishop's current lodger?

10. Name Pam Ewing's brother.

11. Who is Steven Beale's father?

12. Name Pauline and Arthur Fowler's youngest son.

13. Who does Jenny Bradley share a house with in *Coronation Street*?

14. How did Alan Bradley die?

15. What is Beverley from *Neighbours*'s profession?

16. Name the cellar man at the Rovers' Return.

17. Who runs the Woolpack pub in Emmerdale?

18. Which *Coronation Street* character used to run and then edit the *Weatherfield Recorder* before he resigned from the post?
    And which resident of Ramsey Street works as a reporter?

19. Which of the Queen Vic regulars has his beer served to him in his own pewter mug which is kept specially for him behind the bar?

Answers on page 145

BEHIND THE SCENES ON TV / 2

1. Who was John Logie Baird and why is he so important in the history of television?

2. What is an autocue?

3. The first regular colour TV broadcast in Britain took place on 1 July 1967. But can you guess in which decade of the twentieth century the first colour TV broadcast was actually made?

4. What is Cable TV? What is Satellite TV?

5. What is a telethon?

6. It started in a small room in Frith Street, Soho, London in 1926. What was it?

7. Which of the following was not seen during the first week of British television?
   (a) a juggling act
   (b) a man building a sailing ship out of matchboxes
   (c) a flower display
   (d) a wrestling match

8. Television programmes are said to receive Ratings. What are Ratings?

9. In television technology do you know what 'paintbox' is? (Don't panic! – just think about some of the special effects you see on television . . .)

10. A television picture is made up of a certain number of lines. How many lines does a normal British TV image have?
(a) 431
(b) 153
(c) 625
(d) 287

11. What is a Party Political Broadcast?

12. Television is notorious for its use of initials. Some of them, like BBC or ITV, are fairly commonplace. Others are much more complex! Can you guess what the following initials stand for? A little careful thinking, or a good dictionary, should provide you with most of the answers.
(a) ITN
(b) OB
(c) MTV
(d) AFM
(e) VT

13. What do the initials BSB stand for?

14. Can you guess which of the following countries watches more TV than anyone else?
(a) Japan
(b) USA
(c) France
(d) UK
(e) Botswana

15. And finally here's one for the well-travelled experts only! We all know that the BBC and ITV are two of Great Britain's terrestrial TV companies. But can you match the following TV companies up with their respective countries?

(a) Tele 1   Australia
(b) NBC   Germany
(c) ABC   France
(d) ZDF   USA

Answers on page 147

SO YOU
THINK YOU
KNOW
ABOUT MUSIC

?

MUSICAL MYSTERY
TOURS / 1

1. She debutted over twenty years ago with her husband Ike singing 'River Deep Mountain High'. Now she doesn't want to lose you. Who is she?

2. Who went Jazzin' For Blue Jean in the early 1980s?

3. Where did Lisa Stansfield go in search of her baby in 1989?

4. If you gave him ten good reasons to leave him, he'd give you ten good reasons to stay. Who is he?

5. For which film starring actor John Hurt did the

Eurythmics supply the music? Do you know who wrote the book on which the movie was based?

6. Who made their debut in the Cavern Club in Liverpool, and later went on to conquer the world?

7. Who was Bette Midler's pianist and musical arranger in the early 1970s:
   (a) Billy Joel
   (b) Barry Manilow
   (c) Elton John

8. Whose albums have included *Notorious* and *Seven and the Ragged Tiger*?

9. Who could be described as a Moonwalker?

10. The Beatles were probably the most influential pop group of all time. Can you name all four of their members?

11. Which one was murdered in 1980?

12. How do the New Kids on the Block hang?

13. *Ride On Time* was a massive hit for who in 1989?

14. Name George Michael's partner in Wham!

15. Which two groups was Jimmy Sommerville a member of before he went solo?

16. What relation is Billy Jean *not* to Michael Jackson?

17. Which *EastEnders* star had a hit with the song 'Every Loser Wins'?

18. Doctor Robert is the lead singer of which group?

19. Can you match the following stars to the movies for which they provided much of the music?

    (a) Phil Collins   *The Wall*
    (b) Madonna   *Yellow Submarine*
    (c) Pink Floyd   *Buster*
    (d) The Beatles   *Dick Tracy*

20. He was known as the King and he died in 1977. Who was he and was his middle name Aaron, Avon, or Alan?

Answers on page 150

MUSICAL MYSTERY TOURS / 2

1. What was Cliff Richard's first hit record? Do you know in which year it was a hit?

2. She's now married to Mick Jagger of the Rolling Stones, but she used to go out with Bryan Ferry. She's also a talented model and actress in her own right. Who is she?

3. Madonna had a hit called 'Vogue'. What is 'voguing'?

4. Name two of the New Kids on the Block.

5. What was Elton John's first hit record?
   (a) 'Your Song'
   (b) 'Rocket Man'
   (c) 'I'm Still Standing'
   (d) 'Sacrifice'

6. Name the two Pet Shop Boys. Where did they supposedly meet?

7. Kylie Minogue sang 'Tears On My Pillow' in which film?

8. Whose little sister was leaving town in 1990?

9. Why could 'Holding Back The River' be thought of as inappropriate for Marti Pellow's group?

10. The lead singer of the Lilac Time is Stephen Duffy. Of which much more famous Birmingham-based group was he a founder member?

11. Who advised us to Enjoy The Silence while pursuing a Policy of Truth?

12. Who fought for their right to party?

13. Whose albums have included *Sign O' The Times*, *1999* and *Parade*?

14. In the video for which song did Paula Abdul find herself dancing with a cartoon cat?

15. Stock, Aiken and Waterman have been one of the most phenomenally successful production teams in recent years and have provided a score of hits for various artists. Which of the following has never worked with SAW?
(a) Cliff Richard
(b) Big Fun
(c) Jason Donovan
(d) Sonia
(e) Cher

16. Marc Almond recently produced an album of ten songs all written by which late Belgian composer?

17. Who gave us the first of many thousand kisses?

18. Holly Johnson was originally a singer with which controversial Liverpudlian band who had several big hits?

19. Name the Last of the Famous International Playboys.

20. Which former member of the Police has produced several solo albums and has also become an accomplished actor?

Answers on page 152

MUSICAL MYSTERY TOURS / 3

1. Can you identify the following pop stars from their real names?
  (a) George O'Dowd
  (b) Gordon Sumner
  (c) Mary O'Brien

2. The character of Breathless Mahoney was played by which pop star in which movie based on the exploits of a cartoon character?

3. He's married to presenter Paula Yates, and he was a singer in the 1970s with his own group The Boomtown Rats. He now has a solo career, and he's also been honoured by the Queen. Who is he, and why was he honoured?

4. Liza Minnelli is the daughter of which famous Hollywood star?

5. Who might you expect to meet in Paisley Park?

6. She appeared on the very first Top of the Pops in 1964 singing her hit 'I Only Want To Be With You'. Today she's still making the hits and still appearing on *Top of the Pops*. Who is she?

7. Whose albums have included *Ziggy Stardust*, *'Heroes'* and *Modern Love?*

8. This American singer/songwriter sang a song about a Russian city which was originally called Saint Petersburg. Who's the singer and what's the present name of the city?

9. The two Live Aid concerts in 1984 took place in which British and American cities.

10. Who was the only artist who appeared live at both of these events?

11. Which novel by Emily Brontë was the inspiration for Kate Bush's very first Number One hit?

12. What sort of dancing do the Pet Shop Boys get up to?

13. And what sort of dancing does Patrick Swayze get up to?

14. Which pop stars appear in the following films?
    (a) *The Krays*
    (b) *Summer Holiday*
    (c) *Desperately Seeking Susan*
    (d) *Under The Cherry Moon*
    (e) *Give My Regards to Broad Street*
    (f) *Dune*

15. Who checked in at the Heartbreak Hotel in 1956?

Answers on page 154

SO YOU THINK YOU KNOW ABOUT THE MOVIES ?

CINEMA CONUNDRUMS / 1

There's no great mystery how the moving picture you see on the cinema screen is produced – it's basically nothing more than a series of photographs projected at a speed which gives the impression of motion. Of course the pictures are shown at a great speed – at over 16 pictures, or frames, per second. Try it sometime – simply make a series of drawings on separate pieces of paper of a stick figure: if you make each drawing slightly different from the one before then when you flick them quickly one after the other you'll have created the impression of motion. That's the basic principle of cinematography even today.

The cinema as we know it today can be said to have been born in 1895. In that year the French Lumière brothers showed the first ever motion picture to an audience. After some initial suspicion the public warmed to the idea of the 'movies'; in 1911 Hollywood was established as the centre of the US, and later the world, film industry. The leading actors in these pictures – very often short comedy sequences – people such as Charlie Chaplin, Buster Keaton and Mary Pickford, became enormously popular and wealthy stars.

Even though there had been some attempts to show films in synchronization with records, the films remained silent until 1927. Then The Jazz Singer starring singer Al Jolson opened with the words 'You ain't heard nothing yet!' and the film world was changed forever. Now, as well as being able to see their favourite stars in action, people could actually hear them.

Today, not even a hundred years after the motion picture

industry was founded the cinema is one of the most profitable and influential media ever. Hundreds of thousands of people go to the cinema every year, and the stars of the movies are household names. Fortunes are made and lost, and costs of over $50 million to make a film are not uncommon.

Go to the film section of your local library and you will find lots of reference books on the movies. One of the very best, and the most fascinating is The Guinness Book of Movie Facts and Feats, *packed with lots of important and trivial information about the 'silver screen'. If you're ever in London try and visit the Museum of the Moving Image (MOMI) which is the best and most fun-packed museum in the country about the movies and television: they produce an excellent guidebook which is available by post. There are also many movie magazines such as* Empire *packed full of information. But the best way to learn about the movies is to visit the cinema as often as possible!*

1. The hills were alive to what in this popular musical starring Julie Andrews?

2. In which American high school is *Grease* set?

3. Name Roger Rabbit's movie co-star.

4. Which of the following actors has never played the part of James Bond?
   (a) George Lazenby
   (b) Roger Moore
   (c) Pierce Brosnan
   (d) Timothy Dalton

5. What would you expect to have a hundred and one of if you were to meet Cruela de Vil?

6. Who was the French Lieutenant's Woman?

7. 'Raindrops Keep Falling On My Head' was the

theme song from which famous film?

8. What is Superman's only weakness?

9. Who was advised to phone home?

10. Which American detective and comic strip hero was enamoured of Breathless Mahoney but remained faithful to his girlfriend Tess Trueheart?

11. Which two British pop stars took on the roles of real-life criminals Reggie and Ronnie Kray?

12. Where did a party of Australian schoolgirls take a picnic – and were never heard of again?

13. Which Australian actor went 'mad' in the future and then teamed up with pop star Tina Turner to go beyond the Thunderdome?

14. In *Citizen Kane*, one of the most critically acclaimed movies ever, what was Rosebud?

15. Walt Disney's first full-length cartoon was made in 1938 and was an instant success. What was its title?

16. What took place a long, long time ago in a galaxy far away?

17. Who asked us to 'come to the cabaret'?

18. Who was the Man For All Seasons?

19. Which musical, based on Shakespeare's *Romeo and Juliet* featured the feuding between two rival New York street gangs, the Jets and the Sharks?

20. Who is Godzilla?

Answers on page 156

CINEMA CONUNDRUMS / 2

1. Can you match up the following songs from James Bond movies with their singers?
   - (a) 'A View To A Kill'   Gladys Knight
   - (b) 'Diamonds Are Forever' a-Ha
   - (c) 'Licensed To Kill'   Sheena Easton
   - (d) 'The Living Daylights' Duranduran
   - (e) 'For Your Eyes Only'   Shirley Bassey

2. What have doctors, nurses, cowboys, teachers, sergeants, cabbies, and even Cleopatra been advised to do?

3. What was so unusual about the musical *Bugsy Malone*?

4. His name was Quasimodo and he loved a gypsy girl called Esmerelda. Who was he?

5. What sort of creature was Wanda in the film starring John Cleese?

6. What are the Oscars?

7. Who went back to the future three times?

8. She moved out of Ramsey Street and became a Delinquent. Who is she?

9. 'You ain't heard nothin' yet!' Who said these words?

10. What would you dial for murder in the Alfred Hitchcock thriller?

11. Where did Holly Golightly dream of having Breakfast?

12. Which German actress starred in the 1920s movie *The Blue Angel*?

13. Raquel Welch made her starring debut in a film about cavemen. In which year was the film set:
    (a) 1,000 000 BC
    (b) 2,000 000 BC
    (c) 3,000 000 BC

14. What was Doctor Doolittle's peculiar talent?

15. Name Roger Rabbit's wife.

16. Swept from her home in Kansas by a hurricane Dorothy Gale arrived in the Land of Oz. How did she hope to return home?

17. Set in North Africa during the 1940s this is one of the most successful movies ever made. Its two stars are Humphrey Bogart and Ingrid Bergman. The name of the movie is also the name of the town in which most of the action takes place. What's it called?

18. Name four James Bond movies.

19. Can you name all seven of the dwarfs in the Walt Disney film *Snow White and the Seven Dwarfs*?

20. Who are Stadler and Waldorf?

Answers on page 158

CINEMA CONUNDRUMS / 3

1. Throughout the movie *Dick Tracy* our hero was pursued by a faceless villain known only as the Blank. What was the Blank's true identity?

2. Which orphan had a dog called Sandy and believed that 'the sun will come out tomorrow'?

3. What happened to Bambi's mother?

4. Who played the part of Crocodile Dundee?

5. After the Empire struck back who returned?

6. The film *Excalibur* was about the life of which legendary king? And what exactly was Excalibur?

7. Who had Saturday Night Fever and was later to be found Stayin' Alive?

8. What would Freddie give you on Elm Street if you weren't careful?

9. In the movie starring Ted Danson, Steve Gutenberg and Tom Sellick what were the three men left with?

10. What was the only thing which could wake Sleeping Beauty from her enchantment?

11. In the musical based on a book by Charles Dickens who asked for some more?

12. Which pop star played the part of a Man Who Fell To Earth?

13. What creature did Darryl Hannah play in the movie *Splash!*?

14. Which of the following films has never won the Oscar for Best Picture?
    (a) *Gandhi*
    (b) *The Godfather*
    (c) *Chariots of Fire*
    (d) *Sophie's Choice*
    (e) *Rain Man*

15. If you were threatened by a man-eating plant called Audrey Two where would you expect to be?

16. Which film took place in Gotham City?

17. Name Superman's cousin.

18. Who accompanied Dorothy to the Emerald City of Oz?

19. In which film did (a) Dustin Hoffman and (b) Tony Curtis and Jack Lemmon dress up as women?

20. And in which film did Julie Andrews dress up as a man dressed up as a woman!

Answers on page 161

CINEMA CONUNDRUMS / 4

1. Darth Vader was whose father?

2. What did Indiana Jones seek in the Temple of Doom?

3. This former Mister Universe has played the part of a cyborg from the future, a Predator and a Barbarian. What's his name?

4. What giant beast was to be found on Skull Island?

5. *It Couldn't Happen Here* sang these pop stars in the film of the same name. Who are they?

6. These pop stars defeated the Blue Meanies and met Sergeant Pepper's Lonely Hearts Club Band. Who were they and what sort of vehicle did they travel in?

7. How did Professor Henry Higgins attempt to change Eliza Dolittle in *My Fair Lady*?

8. Which of the following films did Marilyn Monroe not star in?
(a) *Some Like It Hot*
(b) *Gentlemen Prefer Blondes*

(c) *The Misfits*
(d) *Meet Me In St Louis*
(e) *The Prince and the Showgirl*

9. Whose girlfriend does Margot Kidder play in a popular series of films?

10. Who framed Roger Rabbit?

11. How did Dumbo fly?

12. *You're The One That I Want* said John Travolta to Olivia Newton-John in which movie?

13. What special ability did Chitty Chitty Bang Bang have?

14. In which Alfred Hitchcock film does a woman get murdered in the shower?

15. Which of the following characters has never appeared in a James Bond film?
    (a) Q
    (b) A
    (c) M

16. Who asked Sam to play it again in which film?

17. Who lost his bike and went on a Big Adventure to find it?

18. Can you name two of the five Marx Brothers?

19. For what part of his anatomy did Daniel Day-Lewis get an Oscar in 1990?

20. Do you know from which movies the following songs come?
(a) 'Bright Eyes'
(b) 'Over the Rainbow'
(c) 'Summer Loving'
(d) 'Climb Every Mountain'
(e) 'What I Did For Love'

Answers on page 163

CINEMA CONUNDRUMS / 5

1. According to the song what does a spoonful of sugar do?

2. Where were Bette Midler and Richard Dreyfuss down and out?

3. What kind of creature is
   (a) Jaws
   (b) Benji
   (c) K9
   (d) King Kong

4. Which comedian, more famous for his portrayal of a tramp, parodied Adolf Hitler in the film *The Great Dictator*?

5. Which actor, more famous for playing the Phantom of the Opera on stage and bumbling Frank Spencer in the TV series *Some Mothers Do 'Ave Them* was Walt Disney's Condorman?

6. Name Tarzan's constant female companion.

7. Can you identify the following Hollywood stars from their real names?
   (a) Frances Ethel Gumm
   (b) Marion Morrison

    (c) Norma Jean Baker
    (d) Maurice Mickelwhite

8. Based on one of the books of the Bible this classic movie starred Charlton Heston and one of its more spectacular special effects was the Parting of the Red Sea. What is it?

9. Can you match the following comic book characters with the actor who played them in the cinema?
    (a) Batman   Jack Nicholson
    (b) Superman   Michael Keaton
    (c) Lex Luthor   Warren Beatty
    (d) Dick Tracy   Christopher Reeve
    (e) The Joker   Gene Hackman

10. What did Doctor Frankenstein create in his laboratory?

11. Jason and his Argonauts set out on a journey in search of what great treasure?

12. At which famous girl's school were the gambling and illegal activities so bad that the police had to be sent in to investigate?

13. Which pop star starred in the film *Purple Rain*?

14. Do you know from which musicals the following songs come?
    (a) 'There Is Nothing Like A Dame'
    (b) 'Don't Rain On My Parade'
    (c) 'Tomorrow'
    (d) 'Evergreen'

15. There have been three films called *A Star Is Born*. Which of the following actresses has not starred in any of them?

    (a) Katharine Hepburn
    (b) Barbra Streisand
    (c) Judy Garland
    (d) Janet Gaynor

16. Who told who 'Frankly my dear I don't give a damn'?

17. In which cult movie would you be encouraged to do the Time Warp?

18. Who learnt to stop worrying and love the bomb?

19. This soul singer became a lady who sang the blues. Do you know the name of either the singer or the part she played in *Lady Sings the Blues*?

20. Who became ET's best human friend?

Answers on page 165

CINEMA CONUNDRUMS / 6

1. Who or what did Danny De Vito and Billy Crystal plan to throw from the train?

2. If you were to make contact with an alien race, what sort of close encounter would it be?

3. Whose wrath did the crew of the USS *Enterprise* face in the second of the *Star Trek* films?

4. Meryl Streep and Roseanne Barr became rivals for the same man in which film?

5. Who was the Rebel Without A Cause?

6. If you faced problems with a haunted house who would you be most likely to call?

7. Who was dreaming of a White Christmas?

8. Mary Poppins believed that the use of this word would make one sound precocious. Which word was it?

9. Which British pop star went on a *Summer Holiday* in 1963 in a double decker bus?

10. What's the name of the Great Mouse Detective?

11. What was the name of the computer in *2001: A Space Odyssey*?

12. Who is Lana Lang?

13. Which British thriller, starring Richard Attenborough and based on a book by Graham Greene, is set in a South England seaside resort?

14. In the 1930s the Joad family set off from Oklahoma to California in search of wealth and a new life. Which film, starring the late Henry Fonda, chronicled the fortunes of the Joad family?

15. Who played the part of Superman's father Jor-El in the first *Superman* film?

Answers on page 168

SO YOU
THINK YOU
KNOW
ABOUT BOOKS
?

BOOK BAFFLERS / 1

It took about 7,000 years for this book to get into your hands . . .

The first method of communication between human beings was probably a series of grunts and growls. But as time passed we began to use different sounds to indicate different objects, ideas or feelings. Still there was no means to record these ideas, until mankind developed an alphabet and a writing system. As in many things, the Chinese seem to have gotten into the act first and the earliest evidence of a written language we have was made between 6,000 and 7,000 years ago in China.

Writing quickly developed and spread throughout most of the civilized world. By the fifteenth century books and manuscripts were commonplace, if only among the educated. Reading and writing were largely the province of educated people such as members of religious orders or great schools and universities. The common people had little access to books and, anyway, were unable to read or write. Books were handwritten, usually by monks, and decorated with elaborate illustrations; it could take years to produce even one book.

The great revolution in book production came at the end of the fifteenth century. The use of moveable type and hand-held presses meant that many copies of books could be produced much more quickly. One of the first books printed using this method was the Bible in the German town of Gutenberg. Even today, an original Gutenberg Bible can *be worth millions of pounds. The first English printer was William Caxton who set up his press in Bruges, Belgium, before moving to England where he started producing books on a regular basis.*

As methods of printing improved and, perhaps more importantly, as more and more people learned to read, so books increased in popularity. In the eighteenth, nineteenth and early twentieth centuries books by favourite authors were awaited with as much excitement as today we might await the latest record by a new pop sensation.

With the coming of television and the cinema, books have certainly declined a little in popularity, even though someone like Barbara Cartland or Jeffrey Archer can still sell over a million copies of each of their titles. But books are still our main source of information and every large and many smaller towns have a well-stocked public library which anyone can use for free. And even many of today's best-loved films and TV series – and even top pop records! – are based on bestselling books. Because after all, whether it's Adrian Mole *or* William Shakespeare, Fungus the Bogeyman *or* Jane Eyre, *books are fun!*

Most of the books which are mentioned in the following questions can be found in the fiction section of your school or local library. To help you along, there's a list of many of the mentioned titles at the end of this section.

1. Name the 'bear of very little brain'.

2. Who went off to Kirrin Island?

3. How old was Adrian Mole when he first began his diary?

4. According to J. R. R. Tolkien what lived in a hole in the ground?

5. It was only a streak of brilliant blue light but it had what peculiar effect on Willie's Grannie Smith?

6. By what name are Pod, Homily and Arrietty better known?

7. What was the Lightning Tree at Follyfoot Farm?

8. What did Jimmy's Uncle Colin from Connecticut send his nephew?

9. She's the strongest girl in the world, lives by herself, and sleeps with her feet on the pillow and her head at the foot of her bed. What's her name?

10. At what time of day would Tom find his garden?

11. Which little girl fell down a rabbit hole, took part in a caucus-race and was given advice by a caterpillar?

12. What's the first name of the disgusting green bogeyman written about by Raymond Briggs?

13. Who took the little boy 'walking through the air' one magic Christmas?

14. The Tin Man, the Cowardly Lion, and the Scarecrow all accompanied this little girl and her dog Toto on her journey. What was the little girl's name and where was she going to?

15. He was the leader of the Lost Boys and refused ever to grow up. His closest friend was the fairy Tinkerbell. Who was he?

16. And what's the name of his archenemy?

17. Which famous detective lived at 221b Baker Street, London?

18. 'Once a king or queen in Narnia, always a King or Queen.' These words were spoken at the coronation of which four kings and queens?

19. Where would you expect to meet Lucy, Linus, Schroder and Woodstock?

20. Why was Adrian Mole suspended from school?

Answers on page 170

WITCHES AND WIZARDS, DUNGEONS AND DRAGONS

1. According to Roald Dahl, these creatures hate children with a 'red-hot sizzling hatred'. They're also indistinguishable from ordinary women. What are they?

2. Who came to 17 Cherry Tree Lane and told Jane and Michael that she would stay there until the wind changed?

3. Name the magician friend of Bilbo Baggins.

4. Who was the Magician's Nephew?

5. 'Mirror, mirror on the wall. Who is the fairest of them all?' Which character would always say these words to her mirror? And what was her mirror's final answer to the question?

6. Where did the Dragonlords live in Anne McCaffrey's series of novels?

7. Which of the children in *The Voyage of the Dawn Treader* was actually turned into a dragon?

8. This legendary magician apparently lived his life

backwards. He also befriended a young boy called 'Wart', who pulled a sword out of a stone and became a King. Who was the magician, and by what name is the boy better known?

9. Who made it 'always winter and never Christmas'?

10. Who were Mrs Whosit, Mrs Whatsit and Mrs Which?

11. Name the Wizard of Earthsea.

12. What precious treasure did Smaug guard?

Answers on page 173

NURSERY RHYMES

Nursery rhymes have been passed down by children throughout the ages, and were often used as skipping chants or in playground games. Many of them are nonsensical jingles, but a surprisingly large proportion are about real historical persons or events. 'Georgie Porgie', for instance, tells us of the life and loves of King George IV who, to say the least, loved the company of women! Another apparently innocent nursery rhyme in this quiz is about the bubonic plague!

There are many collections of nursery rhymes published, but if you're interested in their meanings, the Oxford Dictionary of Nursery Rhymes is a good place to start. Or why not simply sit down and try and work out what some of them mean yourself?

1. How many miles to Babylon?

2. Whom did the singer of the song 'One Misty Moisty Morning' meet one morning?

3. Peter Piper picked a peck of what?

4. When boys and girls come out to play how does the Moon shine?

5. What could Jack Spratt's wife not eat?

6. Where did the woman who had so many children she didn't know what to do live?

7. 'Oranges and lemons,' sang the Bells of St Clement's. What did the Great Bell of Bow say?

8. What are little girls made of?

9. If you were dancing in a ring of roses what would you expect to have a pocketful of?

10. The sparrow, with his bow and arrow, killed Cock Robin. Who saw him die?

11. What frightened away Miss Muffet as she sat on her tuffet?

12. How did contrary Mary's garden grow?

13. He was a merry old soul and called for his pipe and his fiddlers three. Who was he?

14. According to the old rhyme Monday's child is fair of face. What is the child that is born on the Sabbath day?

15. Who chopped off the tails of three blind mice with a carving knife?

16. Who fell down the hill first – Jack or Jill?

17. When the cow jumped over the moon who ran off with the spoon?

18. If you were advised to ride a cock-horse to Banbury Cross what would you expect to see at your destination?

19. How much was the song worth when four and twenty blackbirds were baked in a pie?

20. Some gave them white bread and some gave them brown. Some gave them plum cake and drove them out of town. Who were they?

Answers on page 175

BOOK BAFFLERS / 2

1. Bob and Hilda were just a normal middle-aged couple when the wind blew. What event totally changed their lives?

2. Which trilogy of books introduced the reader to Frodo Baggins, Galadriel, Aragorn and Sauron the Dark Lord?

3. What happened to Alice when she ate the piece of cake labelled 'Eat Me'?

4. Mowgli was the young man-cub deserted in the jungle in *The Jungle Books* by Rudyard Kipling. He was cared for by Baloo and Bagheera. What manner of creatures were Baloo and Bagheera?

5. They've been aloft, afloat and abroad. Who are they?

6. By what collective name were Rebecca, Peter and Phyllis better known after their father disappeared and they went off with their mother to live near a railway station?

7. Mary Lennox was a disagreeable girl. What did she discover at Misselthwaite Manor which so dramatically changed her attitude on life?

8. Which two families set off on a holiday to Lake

Windermere in Arthur Ransome's *Swallows and Amazons*?

9. Can you name four members of the Famous Five?

10. And four members of the Secret Seven?

11. Maid Marian, Little John and Friar Tuck were all members of whose group of outlaws? Do you know in which forest these outlaws made their headquarters?

12. Who came from Asteroid B612, was first seen on Earth in the African desert, and felt responsible for a flower that he had 'tamed'?

13. Who took Pink Rabbit?

14. Which author would tell you to 'go saddle the sea'?

15. Which detective supposedly met his death falling over the Reichenbach Falls in mortal combat with his archenemy Moriarty?

16. Rockingdown, Rat-a-Tat, Rilloby Fair, Ring O' Bells and Ragamuffin. Which is the missing location?

17. How did Captain Hook die?

18. Who did Tintin go looking for in Tibet? And what did he find there?

19. What was the Owl Service?

20. Slartibatfast in *The Hitch-hiker's Guide to the Galaxy* won prizes for the design of what?

Answers on page 177

MYTHS AND LEGENDS

Some of the best stories ever told are to be found in the myths of the Greeks and the Romans. Many of these stories of gods and heroes were told to provide explanations for natural phenomena such as eclipses, or the changing of the seasons; other stories are actually based to some extent or other on fact – for instance, the tale of the Trojan War. The influence of the Greek and Roman myths is enormous; even today we name asteroids and moons in space after gods, following the example of the early astronomers who named the planets.

Many of these stories are to be found in books like The Odyssey *which tells of the fantastic adventures of Ulysses, or* The Illiad *about the Trojan War. The author Roger Lancelyn Green has published many books of myths from many countries. A good modern-day book on the Greek myths is* The God Beneath The Sea *by Leon Garfield; if you're looking for something a little more detailed and comprehensive try* The Greek Myths *by the poet and novelist Robert Graves.*

1. Where did the majority of the Greek Gods live?

2. Name the King and Queen of the Greek Gods.

3. What was to be found in Pandora's Box?

4. King Midas was given a power which, at first

thought, might be everyone's dream. But this blessing turned out to be a curse. What was it?

5. Hades, or Pluto as he was known to the Romans, was the ruler of which land?

6. Ares, or Mars as he was known to the Romans, was the god of what?

7. What was Asgard?

8. Who was the Greek goddess of love?

9. Where was the beautiful Persephone – or Proserpina as she was known to the Romans – forced to live for half of every year?

10. Jason and his crewmen on board *The Argo* sailed the seas in search of which great treasure?

11. She was reputed to be the daughter of a goddess, and was supposedly the most beautiful woman alive. She was also indirectly responsible for the Trojan War. Who was she?

12. The Trojan War was fought between the Greeks and the Trojans and lasted for twelve years. The Greeks finally devised an ingenious way to enter the walled city and defeat their enemies. What was it?

13. Who was the most famous resident of Delphi?

14. With whom did Narcissus fall in love?

15. According to legend who stole from the gods the secret of fire and gave it to man?

16. Daedalus and his son Icarus built for themselves two

pairs of wings with which to fly. What happened to Icarus when he tried to fly?

17. According to Norse mythology, where did heroic warriors go after their death?

18. Why did Orpheus go down into the Underworld?

19. The entrance to the Underworld was guarded by a ferocious three-headed dog. What was his name?

20. Name the god of love.

Answers on page 179

BOOK BAFFLERS / 3

1. This ship's long voyage included visits to the Lone Islands, Deathwater Island, Ramandu's Island and Dragon Island, before some of its crewmembers reached the end of the world. What was the ship's name?

2. Who lived on Sunnybrook Farm?

3. Why did Hazel, Fiver and their fellow rabbits leave their Sandleford home and make for Watership Down?

4. What did Stig find in the dump?

5. For whom did the scarecrow Worzel Gummidge have an unrequited love?

6. Which schoolboy wrote four books about his school, St Custard's, and his friends who included Pearson and Fotherington-Thomas?

7. The pupils of which girls' school were not exactly 'belles', and certainly not ladies, and were much more likely to blow up the chemistry lab with their illegal antics?

8. In his experiments into the dark side of man's nature

what creature did Doctor Henry Jekyll turn himself into?

9. In the trilogy of books by Peter Dickinson, what were the Changes?

10. Who was Sparrowhawk in Ursula le Guinn's series of books set in Earthsea?

11. Smith was a 12-year-old pickpocket in London who saw a man being murdered one fateful day. What important item did Smith take from the man's pocket just before the evil deed took place?

12. What did Jim Hawkins find in old Captain Flint's sea chest?

13. When the clock struck thirteen what could Tom expect to find?

14. In *A Traveller in Time* Penelope Taberner Cameron found herself back in the seventeenth century in Thackers Manor House, where her ancestor once worked. There she learnt of a plot to murder which Queen of Scotland?

15. What was so peculiar about the inhabitants of the land of Lilliput which was discovered by Lemuel Gulliver?

16. Which of Roald Dahl's heroes got himself involved with (a) a giant peach, and (b) a chocolate factory?

17. Which famous song recorded by Kate Bush was based on this novel by Emily Brontë which featured the characters of Cathy and Heathcliff?

18. What kind of animal was My Friend Flicka?

19. Name two of the other participants at the mad tea party attended by Alice when she was in Wonderland.

20. In *The Lord of the Rings* what was Frodo Baggins carrying which was of such great interest and importance to the Dark Lord Sauron?

Answers on page 182

BACK TO THE FUTURE

1. What is a triffid?

2. During the Day of the Triffids almost the entire population of the Earth was blinded. What caused this blindness?

3. Who or what are the Nomes?

4. Why did Arthur Dent become an intergalactic hitch-hiker?

5. How many leagues under the sea did Captain Nemo travel in his submarine *The Nautilus*?

6. In which year did George Orwell's frightening vision of a totalitarian state take place?

7. In which year did Arthur C. Clarke's characters make a Space Odyssey? And in which year did they 'make contact'?

8. Which faraway world was in effect ruled by the sisterhood of the Bene Gesserit, and was plagued by 'sandworms'?

9. Where did Axel Lindenbrok and his uncle travel to in 1863?

10. In the series of books portraying a world ruled by the Tripods what was a Capping?

11. What were so important about the White Mountains in the same series of books?

12. What did Paul Antreides inherit?

13. What manner of creatures did Professor Challenger and his colleagues encounter when they went off in search of the Lost World?

14. Name the arch enemy of the following comic book characters:
    (a) Batman
    (b) Dan Dare
    (c) Flash Gordon
    (d) Superman

15. Who was the Prince In Waiting?

Answers on page 184

THE BARD OF AVON

William Shakespeare is regarded as the greatest dramatist who ever lived. He was born in 1564 in Stratford-on-Avon, and when he was a young man moved down to London. There he joined a company of actors, and began writing plays for them. Most of his plays were seen at the Globe Theatre, a famous theatre on the South Bank of the Thames, which was open to the sky. By the time he died on St George's Day, 23 April 1616 he had enjoyed an enormously successful career as an actor, dramatist and poet, and today is the most performed playwright of all time.

His plays are: Henry VI, Parts I, II and III; The Comedy of Errors; Titus Andronicus; The Two Gentlemen of Verona; The Taming of the Shrew; Love's Labours Lost; Romeo and Juliet; Richard III; Richard II; Henry IV, Parts I and II; King John; Henry V; Julius Caesar; Antony and Cleopatra; Corialanus; The Merry Wives of Windsor; Much Ado About Nothing; The Merchant of Venice; As You Like It; Twelfth Night; A Midsummer Night's Dream; Hamlet; Macbeth; King Lear; Timon of Athens; Troilus and Cressida; All's Well That Ends Well; Measure For Measure; Pericles; Cymbeline; The Tempest; Henry VIII.

The best place to find the answers to the following questions are the plays themselves – your teacher should be able to help you with some of the more difficult ones. Alternatively, an excellent book which tells the stories of Shakespeare's plays is Charles and Mary Lamb's Tales From Shakespeare.

1. Which Queen of Egypt killed herself with a poisonous asp, and why?

2. What is probably Shakespeare's most famous play was set in a castle in Elsinore. Where is Elsinore, and what's the name of the play?

3. Can you pair off these famous lovers?
   - (a) Romeo   Desdemona
   - (b) Othello   Cleopatra
   - (c) Hamlet   Katherina
   - (d) Julius Caesar   Juliet
   - (e) Antony   Calphurnia
   - (f) Petruchio   Ophelia

4. King Lear had three daughters. What were their names?

5. He demanded a pound of flesh from his enemy, Antonio, in old Venice. Who was he and how were his plans thwarted?

6. In which play did three witches gather round a bubbling cauldron to stir up 'double toil and trouble'?

7. Brutus and Cassius conspired to kill which great Roman emperor?

8. In *A Midsummer Night's Dream* Bottom's head was apparently transformed into the head of which other animal?

9. 'Two households, both alike in dignity
   In fair Verona, where we lay our scene,
   From ancient grudge break to new mutiny'
   Who are the families concerned, and in which play do they appear?

10. 'Beware the Ides of March' was a wise piece of advice. Who chose to ignore it?

11. On a blasted heath Macbeth met three witches who made three predictions about his future. What were they?

12. Ophelia was hopelessly in love with Hamlet. Why and how did she die?

13. Who was:
    (a) the Prince of Denmark
    (b) the Moor of Venice
    (c) the Prince of Tyre
    (d) the Merchant of Venice

14. In which play did a young girl and her father become shipwrecked on a uninhabited island?

15. 'This royal throne of kings, this sceptred isle,
    This earth of majesty, this seat of Mars,
    This other Eden, demi-Paradise . . .
    . . . This precious stone set in a silver sea.'
    These words were spoken by John of Gaunt in
    Richard the Second. Of what was he speaking?

16. Which of the following plays was not written by William Shakespeare?
    (a) *As You Like It*
    (b) *The Merry Wives of Windsor*
    (c) *Edward II*
    (d) *Love's Labours Lost*

17. In which Shakespearean play did a prince see the ghost of his father walking the castle ramparts?

18. 'He doth bestride the narrow world
    Like a Colossus; and we petty men

Walk under his huge legs, and peep about
To find ourselves dishonourable graves'
Of whom was Cassius speaking?

19. Who was stabbed through the arras?(!)

20. Can you identify from which Shakespeare play the following famous quotes come?
   (a) 'To be or not to be, that is the question.'
   (b) 'But hark, what light through yonder window breaks?'
   (c) 'The quality of mercy is not strained'
   (d) 'Friends, Romans, countrymen, lend me your ears'
   (e) 'If music be the food of love, play on'
   (f) 'Alas, poor Yorick, I knew him, Horatio'

Answers on page 186

BOOK BAFFLERS / 4

1. Caroline and Mick couldn't leave Dinah. Who was Dinah and why did it seem that they would have to leave her in the book by Mary Treadgold?

2. What was the Psammead?

3. Who lived in a cellar of the Red Lion Tavern with his sisters Miss Fanny and Miss Bridget?

4. In which book written by American writer Madeleine L'Engle did Meg and her friend Calvin travel across space in search of her brother Charles Wallace who had been enslaved by a hideous sentient brain known only as 'It'?

5. Chingahook was the last of which tribe of Indians?

6. In *Animal Farm* what was the name of the pig who took over Manor Farm?

7. This hero of a novel by Rudyard Kipling was brought up as a beggar in India and ended up working for the British secret service as a spy. What was his name?

8. Who was the Prince In Waiting?

9. He had lived for centuries in his castle in Transylvania until he came to nineteenth-century England where he finally met his death at the hands of Doctor Van Helsing. Who was he?

10. Who was hopelessly in love with Pandora at the age of 13¾?

11. Which classic tale told the story of a horse's life – from the horse's point of view?

12. Which Elf lord lived in the Last Homely House East of the Sea?

13. Of what vice was Ebenezer Scrooge cured when he was visited by the Ghosts of Christmases Past, Present and Future?

14. Captain Ahab spent much of his life searching for Moby Dick. Who or what was Moby Dick?

15. In *The War of the Worlds* by H. G. Wells the inhabitants of which planet invaded Earth? And how were the seemingly all-powerful aliens finally defeated?

16. What accident happened to the choirboys in *The Lord of the Flies* which threw them all together?

17. Which animal answered the Call of the Wild in the book of the same title by author Jack London?

18. In what year might Big Brother be watching you?

Answers on page 189

THE CLASSICS

1. Can you match the following classic novels with their opening lines?
   The Novels:
   Moby Dick
   Pride and Prejudice
   A Tale of Two Cities
   Alice's Adventures Through the Looking Glass

   The Opening Lines:
   (a) 'It was the best of times, it was the worst of times.'
   (b) 'Call me Ishmael'
   (c) 'One thing that was certain, that the white kitten had had nothing to do with it.'
   (d) 'It is a truth universally acknowledged that a single man in possession of a good fortune, must be in want of a wife'

2. Who was stranded on a desert island and, after many years of solitude, finally met Friday?

3. 'They seek him here they seek him there.' Who was the object of the French Revolutionaries' pursuit in this novel by the Baroness Orczy?

4. The poet Robert Graves wrote two imaginary autobiographies about the fifth Emperor of Rome

who lived between 10 BC and AD 54. So successful were the novels that they were later made into an equally popular television series. Who was the Roman Emperor?

5. Whom did Bathsheba Everdene marry in Thomas Hardy's novel of country life *Far From The Madding Crowd*?

6. Mild-mannered Mary Shelley, the wife of poet Percy Bysshe Shelley, was charged with the task of telling a ghost story to a group of friends. In doing so she produced one of the best horror novels ever and inspired countless hundreds of horror movies in the twentieth century. Her book was subtitled *The Modern Prometheus*; by what name is it more commonly known?

7. For whom did Jane Eyre go to work as a governess?

8. Charles Dickens was undoubtedly the most popular novelist of his day. When he died at the age of 58 he had written over fifteen novels and had created some of the most memorable characters ever to appear in English fiction. Can you match up the following characters with the novels in which they appear?
   (a) Tiny Tim   *Oliver Twist*
   (b) Miss Haversham   *David Copperfield*
   (c) The Artful Dodger *The Old Curiosity Shop*
   (d) Peggoty   *A Christmas Carol*
   (e) Little Nell   *Great Expectations*

9. Name the book by Aldous Huxley which paints a frightening picture of a future world in which most people are subservient to the state and addicted to a drug called *soma*.

10. What was the name of the old dark house in which Titus Groan lived in the books by writer and artist Mervyn Peake?

11. Who went on a search for the lost treasure of King Solomon's Mines in H. Rider Haggard's famous novel?

12. Who was the murderer of the Rue Morgue in Edgar Allan Poe's story?

13. Who killed Edwin Drood in Charles Dickens' *The Mystery of Edwin Drood*?

14. How many rings of power were made in J. R. R. Tolkien's *The Lord of the Rings*?

Answers on page 191

These are just some of the books mentioned in the previous quizzes, and are some of my favourites. They're all available at your local library; why not ask your librarian or teacher for other books by the same author?

The Hitch-hiker's Guide to the Galaxy	Douglas Adams
Go Saddle The Sea	Joan Aiken
Watership Down	Richard Adams
Peter Pan	J. M. Barrie
Five On Treasure Island	Enid Blyton
The Rub A Dub Mystery	Enid Blyton
Fungus the Bogeyman	Raymond Briggs
When the Wind Blows	Raymond Briggs
Wuthering Heights	Emily Brontë
The Secret Garden	Frances Hodgson Burnett
Alice's Adventures in Wonderland and *Through the Looking Glass*	Lewis Carroll
The Tripods Trilogy	John Christopher
2001: A Space Odyssey	Arthur C. Clarke
The Last of the Mohicans	James Fennimore Cooper
James and the Giant Peach	Roald Dahl
Charlie and the Chocolate Factory	Roald Dahl
Robinson Crusoe	Daniel Defoe
A Christmas Carol	Charles Dickens
David Copperfield	Charles Dickens
Cobbler's Dream (Follyfoot)	Monica Dickens

The Adventures of TR Bear	Terrance Dicks
The Changes Trilogy	Peter Dickinson
The Adventures of Sherlock Holmes	Sir Arthur Conan Doyle
Worzel Gummidge	Barbara Ephran Taylor
The God Beneath The Sea	Leon Garfield
Smith	Leon Garfield
The Owl Service	Alan Garner
Dune	Frank Herbert
The Adventures of Tintin	Herge
The Jungle Books	Rudyard Kipling
Kim	Rudyard Kipling
Stig of the Dump	Clive King
A Wrinkle In Time	Madeleine L'Engle
The Lion, The Witch and the Wardrobe	C. S. Lewis
The Magician's Nephew	C. S. Lewis
Pippi Longstocking	Astrid Lindgren
The Railway Children	E. Nesbit
Five Children and It	E. Nesbit
The Borrowers	Mary Norton
Animal Farm	George Orwell
1984	George Orwell
Tom's Midnight Garden	Philippa Pearce
Truckers	Terry Pratchett

Swallows and Amazons	Arthur Ransome
Black Beauty	Anna Sewell
Frankenstein	Mary Shelley
Doctor Jekyll and Mister Hyde	Robert Louis Stevenson
Dracula	Bram Stoker
Gulliver's Travels	Jonathan Swift
Down With Skool!	Searle and Willans
The Hobbit	J. R. R. Tolkien
The Lord of the Rings	J. R. R. Tolkien
The Secret Diary of Adrian Mole	Sue Townsend
We Couldn't Leave Dinah	Mary Treadgold
A Traveller in Time	Alison Uttley
20,000 Leagues Under The Sea	Jules Verne
The War of the Worlds	H. G. Wells

THE
ANSWERS

1. Four. The blue and silver badges are given for submitting interesting ideas and letters to the programme, the gold for extra-special achievement, and the green one for helping to preserve the environment. *Blue Peter* is one of the BBC's most successful children's programmes ever and was first seen on 16 October 1958; its first presenters were Christopher Trace, an actor, and Leila Williams, Miss Great Britain of 1957!

2. *Coronation Street.* The Rover's Return, Alf's Mini-Market and The Kabin are run by Alec and Bet Gilroy, Alf Roberts, and Rita Fairclough respectively. The first episode of *Coronation Street* was seen on 9 December 1960 and was originally to have been called *Florizel* or *Jubilee Street*!

3. *Record Breakers.* Castle himself is a record breaker and holds the world record for tap-dancing a million taps in just under twenty-four hours!

4. *Why Don't You Switch Off Your Television Set And Do Something More Interesting Instead?*

5. *Blankety Blank*, one of the most popular game shows on television and which has been seen every year since 1979!

6. Phillip Schofield.

7. *That's Life!* Esther Rantzen's programme was first seen in 1973.

8. Actor Sylvester McCoy. He's of course more famous for playing the title role of *Doctor Who*.

9. The Play Bus.

10. Manuel in *Fawlty Towers* the immensely successful comedy series starring John Cleese. Andrew Sachs, the actor who plays Spanish Manuel, was actually born in Berlin!

11. (a) *EastEnders;* (b) *Neighbours;* (c) *Coronation Street*

12. Sesame Street.

13. Because he was found by Mr Brown at Paddington Railway Station in London.

14. Bungle.

15. Anneke Rice.

16. *Top of the Pops.*

17. Sir Jimmy Saville.

18. From Manchester.

19. Fashion – they're both presenters on *The Clothes Show.*

20. *Open Air*

1. Orville

2. Her wrinkled stockings.

3. Frank Spencer, played by actor Michael Crawford in the series *Some Mothers Do 'Ave Them*. Crawford is an accomplished actor and singer and was the original Phantom of the Opera in Andrew Lloyd-Webber's musical.

4. Roland Rat.

5. Hamburgers.

6. Audrey fforbes-Hamilton, played by Penelope Keith in the series *To The Manor Born*.

7. Dame Edna Everage. Dame Edna is played by talented comedian Barry Humphries, whose other creations include Sir Les Paterson, the Australian 'Cultural Attaché'.

8. Madge Allsop.

9. Edd the Duck. So far he's driven several BBC TV Children's Presenters quite insane! Edd is six years old and says he's the greatest TV personality in the history of television.

10. The benevolent witch in the series of the same name and played by Elisabeth Estensen and Georgina Hale.

11. Ronnie Corbett and Ronnie Barker.

12. (a) Mork and Mindy; (b) Morecambe and Wise; (c) Cannon and Ball; (d) French and Saunders.

13. Basil Brush.

14. Del Trotter in *Only Fools And Horses*.

15. An Earth spacecraft, whose entire crew was killed by a radiation leak.

16. The Fraggles.

17. Scrappy-Doo.

18. Jim Davidson.

19. Fawlty Towers. Despite only thirteen episodes ever having been made of this series in 1975 and 1979 *Fawlty Towers* is still one of the most repeated and best-loved comedy series ever made. This is due greatly to the comic talents of John Cleese who played hotel owner Basil Fawlty and who was also one of the mainstays of the groundbreaking comedy in the sixties, *Monty Python's Flying Circus*.

20. Milliway's, the Restaurant at the End of the Universe.

ADVENTURES IN SPACE – PAGE 19

1. *Doctor Who*, one of the BBC's most popular series which has been seen regularly on the television screens since 1963!

2. Flash Gordon, the Phantom and Mandrake the Magician

3. Kappapoto

4. R2D2 and C3PO.

5. The Terrahawks are: Doctor Tiger Ninestein; Mary Falconer; Kate Kestrel; Hawkeye; and Lieutenant Hiro.

6. Zelda; her son is called Yung Star.

7. Michael Landon.

8. Whenever he becomes angry he turns into the Incredible Hulk.

9. Lady Penelope, the London agent of International Rescue in *Thunderbirds*.

10. Captain James T. Kirk; Mister Spock; 'Bones' McCoy; Scotty; Lieutenant Uhura; Mister Sulu; and Mister Chekhov.

11. Dave Lister, Arnold Rimmer, Cat, Creighton and Holly.

12. Superboy.

13. *Star Trek – The Next Generation.*

14. Marina.

15. A nuclear disaster blasted the Moon away from the Earth's orbit and sent it on an aimless journey through space.

1. *Dallas* is set in Texas.

2. Denver, Colorado.

3. Weatherfield.

4. Walford.

5. Summer Bay.

6. They met when Scott tried to stop Charlene from what, he believed, was breaking and entering.

7. Brisbane in Queensland, East Australia.

8. Tracey Barlow, whose mother is Deirdre.

9. Nick Cotton. He wanted to get his hands on the £10,000 Dot Cotton had won.

10. Alexis.

11. *The Colbys.*

12. Alexis and Dex.

13. Henry.

14. Aunt Edie

15. Queen Victoria.

16. Sally Webster.

17. *Crossroads.*

18. Madge.

1. (a) Bob Holdness – *Blockbusters;* (b) Michael Parkinson – *Give Us A Clue*; (c) Henry Kelly – *Going For Gold;* (d) Les Dawson – *Blankety Blank.*

2. Bruce Forsyth who presents *The Generation Game.*

3. (a) The Hardacres in *Brass*
   (b) The Boswells in *Bread*
   (c) The Sugdens in *Emmerdale*
   (d) The Macdonalds in *Coronation Street*
   (e) The Ewings in *Dallas.*

4. Noel Edmonds.

5. *Bullseye.*

6. *Surprise! Surprise!*

7. Les Dawson.

8. David Coleman.

9. (a) Snorbet
   (b) Little Willie
   (c) K9

10. *Motormouth*

11. *The Eurovision Song Contest.* Great Britain has won the competition three times: in 1966 with Sandy

Shaw singing *Puppet On A String;* in 1969 with Lulu singing *Boom Bang A Bang Bang;* and in 1979 with Buck's Fizz singing *Making Your Mind Up.* The closest Cliff has got is second place in 1967 with a song called *Congratulations.*

12. U.N.C.L.E. Napoleon Solo and Ilya Kuryakin were played by actors Robert Vaughan and David McCallum, and the word U.N.C.L.E. stands for United Nations Command for Law Enforcement.

13. Esther Rantzen

14. *Fourth Dimension.* Caron is the daughter of Gloria Hunniford.

15. Terry Wogan. He was later succeeded by Les Dawson.

16. Animals.

17. The dog was called Dougal and the cow was called Ermintrude.

18. Zebedee.

19. 'Def' is short for 'definitely', a slang term meaning important or crucial.

20. Magnus Magnusson, the quizmaster on *Mastermind.*

CARTOON CAPERS / 1 – PAGE 26

1. Popeye. He gains his amazing strength from eating spinach – try it, it's good for you!

2. Olive Oyl.

3. Scooby-Doo.

4. Roadrunner.

5. (a) Rocky; (b) Boo Boo; (c) Barney Rubble (Fred's wife is called Wilma and their daughter is Pebbles); (d) Minnie Mouse (Mickey's other best friend is Donald Duck).

6. Donald Duck.

7. Central Organization of Police Specialists.

8. Michelangelo, Raphael, Leonardo and Donatello. The Turtles might not be the best painters in the world but they all take their names from four very famous Italian artists who all lived in fifteenth-century Florence!

9. Poddington Peas.

10. Rupert The Bear.

11. Skeletor is the enemy of He-Man and the Masters of the Universe. He-Man and his friends were originally

toys before their adventures were transferred to television and then to the television screen.

12. Bugs Bunny.

13. Snoopy. The cartoon series is called *Peanuts* and its artist, Charles Schulz, is one of the most successful cartoonists ever; but originally Schultz didn't want to call the strip *Peanuts*: he wanted to call it *Little Folk*! Other members of the Peanuts gang include Lucy, Linus, Schroeder, Marcie and Peppermint Patty.

14. Tintin. Tintin's probably the most famous French cartoon character ever, even though his creator, Herge, was Belgian!

15. The Wombles. Their great uncle is Uncle Bulgaria and these furry creatures first appeared in books written by Elizabeth Beresford, before their adventures transferred to the television screen. On television their stories are told by actor Bernard Cribbins: in the 1970s they even formed their own pop group, singing songs written by composer Mike Batt! Because of their keeness in collecting rubbish these furry creatures have often been used in litter collecting campaigns.

1. The British Broadcasting Corporation. The BBC, or the British Broadcasting Company as it was then known, was formed in 1922 and began regular radio broadcasts in that year. In 1936 it started a regular television service and in 1964 BBC2 was launched. The first colour broadcast was made in 1967, and regular colour broadcasts began in 1970. BBC Television is divided into several geographical regions which produce local programmes, in addition to programmes which are shown nationally.

As well as BBC1 and BBC2 the BBC operates five national radio stations – Radios 1, 2, 3, 4 and 5 – plus many other local radio stations, as well as the World Service which broadcasts to many different countries every day in their own languages. It also has a division, BBC Enterprises, which produces books and other similar merchandise. The BBC is run by a Board of Governors, which includes a Director General and a Chairman. Unlike ITV the BBC is not allowed to carry commercials, and is financed largely by the Licence Fee.

2. On 2 November 1936. Some of the first acts to appear on television included a pair of Chinese jugglers and a comic duo called Buck and Bubbles.

3. They are all members of the Independent Television body. This is a group of about fifteen stations, financed largely by TV commercials, which make programmes for certain local areas of the country, as well as programmes which are broadcast nationally. ITV started broadcasting in September 1955, and, unlike the BBC, was allowed to carry advertisements.

4. TV-AM. TV AM was originally fronted by television presenters David Frost, Angela Rippon, Peter Jay, Anna Ford and Robert Kee, and it first began broadcasting in 1983.

5. This is an annual fee which everyone who owns and operates a television set must pay. The fee varies, depending on whether you have a colour or a black-and-white TV set. The BBC, which is not allowed to accept advertisements, is financed mainly by this money.

6. The Open University was set up in the 1960s and is a system whereby one can study for a university degree at home. The University's 'lectures' are shown on the BBC.

7. The wedding of Prince Charles to Lady Diana Spencer at St Paul's Cathedral.

8. The *Live Aid* concerts in London and Philadelphia in aid of the victims of the Ethiopian famine. These concerts were watched by over 1.6 billion people in the world!

9. The Brits. Recent winners of the Brits Awards include Phil Collins and Kate Bush.

10. The business of the House of Commons. Before 1989 one could only listen to the proceedings of the House of Commons on the radio.

11. The Director General is a member of the BBC's Board of Governors, and together with the Chairman

is responsible for the BBC's day-to-day policies and programming. At the time of going to press the Director General of the BBC is Michael Checkland.

12. The television stations – at the time of going to press! – are Anglia TV (for the East of England); Border TV (the Borders and the Isle of Man); Central TV (East and West Midlands); Channel TV (the Channel Islands); Grampian TV (North Scotland); Granada TV (North-West England); HTV (Wales and West England); London Weekend Television (the London area at the weekend); Scottish TV (Central Scotland); TVS (South and South-East England); TSW (South-West England); Tyne Tees TV (North-East England); Ulster TV (Northern Ireland); Yorkshire TV (Yorkshire). Channel Four, which is based in London and was formed in 1982, makes hardly any programmes itself, but commissions production companies to make them for nationwide broadcasting.

13. (a) Levi jeans
    (b) British Telecom
    (c) Milk Tray chocolates
    (d) PG Tips tea
    The cost to an advertising company for a commercial depends upon the length of the commercial and the time when it is shown. For instance, a commercial shown just before *Coronation Street* which can attract up to 17 million viewers will cost much more than one shown before a programme which only attracts 3 million viewers. Certain products, such as cigarettes, may not be advertised on television.

14. 21 July 1969. The mission to land a man on the Moon was called Apollo Eleven. The very first man on the moon was Neil Armstrong, who stepped down from the Lunar Module saying the historic words

'That's one small step for a man, but a giant leap for mankind.'

15. BBC Television. It closed down on 1 September 1939 as the Second World War began – it was thought that the German bombers would be able to home into the television transmitters in their bombing campaign. The last thing to be seen on British television before war broke out was a Mickey Mouse cartoon. The Second World War ended in 1945 and television returned the following year.

1. In a vetinary practice in the Yorkshire Dales, in the series *All Creatures Great and Small*. James Herriot, himself a real-life vet, wrote the books on which this series is based.

2. The Twist Family in the Australian comedy series *Round The Twist*.

3. Peggy, played by actress Su Pollard, finally put on a Yellowcoat in the very last episode of *Hi De Hi*.

4. René's café in *'Allo 'Allo*. The series *'Allo 'Allo* is set during the years of the Second World War when France was occupied by the German Army, and many French people were members of the Resistance. The Germans invaded France in 1940 and were defeated in that country in 1944. The Second World War finally ended in 1945.

5. Sergeant Bilko, as played by American comedian Phil Silvers.

6. Top Cat, or Boss Cat. The *Top Cat* cartoon series can be said to have many similarities to the *Bilko* TV series: in fact, some of the voices of the characters belong to actors from the *Bilko* series!

7. *Blackadder*. Over the centuries we've seen the exploits of Blackadder and his descendants in the

Dark Ages, at the Court of Queen Elizabeth I, in Regency England, in the trenches of the First World War and, in a Christmas special, in Dickensian London. The Blackadder in each series has been played by Rowan Atkinson.

8. Joey, Jack, Adrian, Aveline and Billy.

9. *Dad's Army*. The regular members of this branch of the home guard included Captain Mainwaring, Sergeant Wilson, and Privates Jones, Godfrey, Pike, Fraser and Walker.

10. Mobile Army Surgical Hospital. M*A*S*H was probably the most successful comedy series ever: its final episode in 1983 was watched by over 125 million people in the United States alone. The series was set during the Korean War, which was a war between North and South Korea in which American soldiers were involved. The war took place between 1950 and 1953 – the M*A*S*H TV series actually lasted longer than the war in which it was set!

11. Russ Abbott.

12. (a) *Hi De Hi*; (b) *Spatz*; (c) *'Allo 'Allo*.

13. Lilo Lil, her husband's Irish girlfriend.

14. *The Munsters*.

15. Australia. The name of their touring van is Bedford, but he's affectionately known as the Winjin' Pom.

16. *The Golden Girls*.

17. *Porridge*.

18. Sharon and Tracy.

19. Comic Relief.

20. Tom and Barbara Good (played by Richard Briers and Felicity Kendall); and Jerry and Margo Ledbetter (played by Paul Eddington and Penelope Keith).

1. William Roach who plays the character of Ken Barlow.

2. Adam, Steven, Fallon and Amanda.

3. Fallon.

4. She met him when she was modelling for the advertisement for a perfume he was promoting.

5. Damon. He was stabbed in York.

6. Ailsa Stuart.

7. Scott Robinson. He was, of course, replaced by Jason Donovan.

8. It turned out that his death had been part of Pam's dream.

9. Skinner.

10. He was stabbed outside a disco.

11. Wendy Crozier.

12. Frank Morgan.

13. *Neighbours.*

14. To marry.

15. *Coronation Street.*

16. Lenny.

17. Kristin.

18. Craig Maclachlan. His band is called Check One-Two.

1. Esther Rantzen.

2. Angela Rippon.

3. Sue Lawley.

4. Hudson and Hall.

5. Thora Hird.

6. Harry Secombe.

7. Michaela Strachan.

8. Helen Rollason.

9. Julian Clary (and Fanny, the wonderdog).

10. Jeremy Beadle.

LAW AND ORDER –
PAGE 39

1. Hercule Poirot and Miss Marple who have most recently been played by David Suchet and Joan Hickson respectively. Agatha Christie wrote over eighty detective novels, some of the most famous of which are *The Murder of Roger Acroyd, Murder On The Orient Express* and *Death On The Nile*. She also wrote romantic novels, and her mystery play, *The Mousetrap* is the longest-running play in the world. Agatha Christie died in 1976.

2. Hartley Police Station.

3. Crime and mystery novels, in the series *Murder, She Wrote*.

4. Maddie Hayes; her colleague is David Addison.

5. Hannibal Smith.

6. *T. J. Hooker*.

7. Because of his hideous physical appearance.

8. Cagney and Lacey.

9. Inspector Clouseau.

10. In the Hill Street police station.

11. Inspector Macduff.

12. Michael Caine.

13. Sheena Easton. She's of course much more famous as a pop singer and has had many hit records, as well as singing with stars the like of Prince. She was 'discovered' by Esther Rantzen on her BBC TV Programme *The Big Time*.

14. In *Baywatch*.

15. *Bergerac*.

16. *Inspector Morse*.

17. *The Avengers* and *The New Avengers*.

18. At the Old Bailey.

19. Sun Hill police station.

20. Brian Glover.

CARTOON CAPERS / 2 –
PAGE 42

1. Bananaman.

2. Captain Pugwash.

3. Inspector Clouseau. Clouseau first appeared in the
   Pink Panther series of movies, before turning up in
   the cartoon series; in the movies he was played by
   actor Peter Sellers.

4. Bananaman.

5. Pizza.

6. A cat.

7. Terry Wogan.

8. Tweety-Pie, the bird. Tom's arch enemy is Jerry, the
   mouse.

9. Laurel and Hardy.

10. Barney Rubble from *The Flintstones*. The Flintstones
    lived in the town of Bedrock, and their cartoon
    adventures are also to be seen in a live-action
    cinema movie.

11. Defenders of the Earth.

12. Ming the Merciless.

13. Schroeder, the little boy who plays the piano and whose hero is the composer Beethoven.

14. Noggin the Nog.

15. A skunk.

TELEVISUAL TEASERS / 3 – PAGE 44

1. (a) Cheers
   (b) The Queen Vic in *EastEnders*
   (c) The Rover's Return in *Coronation Street*
   (d) The Woolpack in *Emmerdale*

2. Jeremy Beadle.

3. Sir Jimmy Saville.

4. *Points of View.*

5. Lizzie Webb.

6. Edward Heath. Edward Heath was Prime Minister of Britain between 1970 and 1974. He's also an accomplished musician and sailor.

7. Hilda Ogden, as played by Jean Alexander. Hilda had come back briefly to see her old friends.

8. Jonathan Ross, who presents the chat show *The Last Resort.*

9. (a) Detective Inspector Burnside – *The Bill.*
   (b) Bruce Wayne – *Batman.*
   (c) Stavros – *Kojak*
   (d) Sonny Crockett – *Miami Vice*
   (e) Norman Stanley Fletcher – *Porridge*
   (f) Jessica Fletcher – *Murder, She Wrote*

10. Antoine de Caunes

11. Cilla Black. She's now better known as the presenter of *Blind Date* and *Surprise! Surprise!*

12. Mork, in *Mindy and Mork*.

13. It 'helps to make a brighter day' – according to the theme song from *Neighbours!*

14. Sir Humphrey Appleton, played by actor Nigel Hawthorne. *Yes, (Prime) Minister* is supposedly Mrs Thatcher's favourite programme!

15. The Romulans – they are the enemy of Captain Kirk and the Federation in *Star Trek*.

1. Ethel Skinner.

2. Pat Wicks.

3. Alf and Audrey.

4. J. R. Ewing and Sue Ellen.

5. 150,000 Australian dollars.

6. Jock Ewing died in a plane crash.

7. Scott.

8. Clayton Farlow.

9. She's a motor mechanic.

10. Ethel Skinner's in *EastEnders*.

11. Joe Mangel's in *Neighbours*.

12. Erinsborough.

13. Bobby Ewing, who is played by actor Patrick Duffy who starred in *The Man From Atlantis*

14. Doctor Legge.

15. A statue of the Greek philosopher Plato. Henry and Joe Mangel accidentally broke off the nose and tried to replace it with one made of plaster of Paris!

16. Kevin and Sally Webster.

17. Caress Morell.

18. Zach Powers.

1. A member of the gang he used to work for shot him by a canal.

2. Mrs Gunnerson.

3. The Enisborough News.

4. (a) Kevin – Sally; (b) Des – Steph; (c) Derek – Mavis; (d) Alf – Audrey; (e) Jack – Vera; (f) Alec – Bet.

5. Ian Beale.

6. Nell.

7. Kenny.

8. Terry Duckworth. The Duckworths' lodger is Curly Watts.

9. Percy Sugden.

10. Cliff Barnes.

11. Simon Wicks.

12. Martin.

13. She shares a house with Felicity Khan.

14. He was knocked down by a tram in Blackpool when he was chasing Rita Fairclough.

15. A doctor.

16. Jack Duckworth.

17. Amos Brierley.

18. Ken Barlow. Scott Robinson.

19. Pete Beale.

1. John Logie Baird, a former socks salesman (!) from Scotland was the man who invented television, or 'seeing by wireless', as it was known. Baird died in 1946.

2. An autocue is a device placed directly by a television camera and which displays the words a television presenter has to say on camera, thereby making it unnecessary for the presenter constantly to refer to his notes or look down at his script.

3. The first colour TV broadcast was actually demonstrated in 1928 by John Logie Baird!

4. Cable TV is transmitted to homes which are on, and have paid for, a cable network, transmitted by underground cables. Satellite TV is beamed directly from satellites in space to special receivers. Cable and Satellite TV provide a further selection of programmes to complement the existing Earth bound, or terrestrial, TV channels, like the BBC or ITV.

5. Telethons originated in America and are television programmes, usually lasting many hours, which are devoted to raising money for various deserving charities. The BBC's *Children In Need* appeal, which raises tens of millions of pounds every year, is a good example of a British telethon.

6. Television. John Logie Baird gave the first public demonstration of television on 26 January 1926 in a small back room in London's Frith Street.

7. (d) A wrestling match.

8. The Ratings are a means to determine how many viewers are watching a certain programme. This is done by means of a special meter attached to television sets in a set number of houses and which record the programmes being viewed. So if, say, 55% of the selected families are watching a programme at any one time it can safely be said that 55% of the wider viewing public are watching the same programme.

9. Paintbox, or Quantel as it is sometimes known, is a computer system used primarily for special effects. Using a light pen on a computer screen the designers can, for example, change the colour of various objects on screen and create complicated on-screen graphics.

10. At the moment British television has (c) 625 lines.

11. A Party Political Broadcast is a programme presented by a political party to give that party's particular point of view. Each party is limited to a certain number of broadcasts a year, determined by the number of votes they received at the last general election. Party political broadcasts are seen on each of the four terrestrial channels.

12. (a) Independent Television News
    (b) Outside Broadcast
    (c) Music Television
    (d) Assistant Floor Manager
    (e) Video Tape

13. British Satellite Broadcasting, a company which

began broadcasting five new television channels from space in 1990.

14. The Japanese watch on average eight hours of TV a day – that's 2,920 hours a year! In comparison the British only watch about three hours a day, or twenty-one hours a week.

15. (a) Tele 1 – France; (b) NBC – USA; (c) ABC – Australia (America also has a channel called ABC); (d) ZDF – Germany

MUSICAL MYSTERY TOURS / 1 – PAGE 55

1. Tina Turner.

2. David Bowie.

3. 'All Around the World'.

4. Jason Donavon.

5. *1984.* The original book was written by George Orwell.

6. The Beatles.

7. (b) Barry Manilow.

8. Duranduran.

9. Michael Jackson.

10. John Lennon, Paul McCartney, George Harrison and Ringo Starr. The Beatles' original drummer was Pete Best, but he was replaced by Ringo Starr before the group hit the big time.

11. John Lennon. He was murdered outside the Dakota Building in New York where he lived.

12. Tough, as in the title of one of their hit singles.

13. Black Box.

14. Andrew Ridgeley.

15. Bronski Beat and the Communards.

16. She's not his lover.

17. Nick Berry who plays the part of Wicksy in the top-rated soap.

18. The Blow Monkeys.

19. (a) Phil Collins – *Buster*; (b) Madonna – *Dick Tracy*; (c) Pink Floyd – *The Wall*; (d) The Beatles – *Yellow Submarine*.

20. His full name was Elvis *Aaron* Presley.

1. *Move It* in 1958!

2. Jerry Hall.

3. A dance, which originated in New York, and which involves the dancer striking various 'fashion' poses while dancing.

4. Donnie Wahlberg; Jordan Knight; Joseph McIntyre; Jonathan Knight; Danny Wood.

5. (b) *Your Song*. *Sacrifice*, however, was his first Number One hit.

6. Neil Tennant and Chris Lowe. They supposedly met in a record shop in London.

7. *The Delinquents.*

8. Tanita Takaram's.

9. Marti sings in the group Wet, Wet, Wet!

10. Duranduran – in the days before they were famous!

11. Depeche Mode.

12. The Beastie Boys.

13. Prince.

14. 'Opposites Attract'

15. (e) Cher.

16. Jacques Brel, whose best known song is probably 'If You Go Away'

17. Fairground Attraction: *The First of a Million Kisses* is the title of their first album.

18. Frankie Goes To Hollywood.

19. Morrisey.

20. Sting. His most famous appearance in the cinema was in the science-fiction epic *Dune*, but he has also played alongside Meryl Streep in *Plenty*.

1. (a) Boy George; (b) Sting; (c) Dusty Springfield

2. Madonna in the movie *Dick Tracy*.

3. Bob Geldof. He was created a Knight of the British Empire for the money he raised for the starving people of Ethiopia by organising Band Aid and Live Aid.

4. Judy Garland. Liza has, of course, most recently sung with the Pet Shop Boys.

5. Prince.

6. Dusty Springfield.

7. David Bowie.

8. Billy Joel; the city's modern name is Leningrad.

9. London and Philadelphia.

10. Phil Collins.

11. *Wuthering Heights*.

12. Domino Dancing.

13. Dirty Dancing!

14. (a) Martin and Gary Kemp; (b) Cliff Richard;

(c) Madonna; (d) Prince; (e) Paul McCartney; (f) Sting.

15. Elvis Presley.

1. *The Sound of Music*, which was the true story of the Von Trapp family, who escaped the Germans when they invaded Austria in 1938 and fled to Switzerland.

2. Rydell High.

3. Baby Herman.

4. (c) Pierce Brosnan, who in fact narrowly missed taking over the part from Roger Moore (the part was given to Timothy Dalton). George Lazenby played the part of 007 in only one film. The James Bond movies and character are based on a series of books by Ian Fleming – who also wrote *Chitty Chitty Bang Bang*!

5. Dalmations. Cruela de Vil was the evil dognapper in Walt Disney's *One Hundred and One Dalmations*, based on the book by Dodie Smith.

6. Meryl Streep, who played the role of Sarah. The film is based on a novel of the same name by John Fowles.

7. *Butch Cassidy and the Sundance Kid*, starring Robert Redford and Paul Newman. Butch Cassidy and the Sundance Kid were real-life bank and train robbers in North America in the 1890s.

8. Kryptonite – irradiated chunks of his home world

Krypton. The Superman movies are all based on the series of popular American comics which began in 1938.

9. ET, the ExtraTerrestrial in Steven Spielberg's blockbuster movie.

10. Dick Tracy.

11. Gary and Martin Kemp of Spandau Ballet.

12. At Hanging Rock.

13. Mel Gibson, who played the part of Mad Max in three films.

14. Rosebud was the name of Citizen Kane's childhood sled. The film *Citizen Kane* starring and directed by Orson Welles is supposed to be based on the life of a millionaire publisher and recluse, William Randolph Hearst, and is generally supposed to be one of the greatest films of all time.

15. *Snow White and the Seven Dwarfs.*

16. *Star Wars* and its two sequels, *The Empire Strikes Back* and *The Return of the Jedi.*

17. Liza Minnelli who played the part of singer Sally Bowles in *Cabaret*. Liza is the daughter of Judy Garland (Dorothy in *The Wizard of Oz*) and has, of course, also recorded with the Pet Shop Boys.

18. Sir Thomas More, who was played by Paul Schofield in the film version of the play by Robert Bolt. The real-life Sir Thomas More was executed by Henry VIII in 1535, when he refused to accept Henry as head of the Church in England.

19. *West Side Story.*

20. A giant radioactive dinosaur-like creature, who has terrorized Japan in numerous Japanese films. He has even had a run in with King Kong!

1. (a) 'A View to A Kill' – Duranduran; (b) 'Diamonds Are Forever' – Shirley Bassey (the only person to have recorded two James Bond themes, the other being 'Goldfinger'); (c) 'Licensed to Kill' – Gladys Knight; (d) 'The Living Daylights' – a-Ha; (e) 'For Your Eyes Only' – Sheena Easton.

2. Carry on. *Carry on, Doctor, Nurse* etc. have all been titles of the phenomenally successful *Carry On* series of films. They have featured such talented comedy actors as Kenneth Williams, Sid James, Kenneth Connor, Joan Sims and Barbara Windsor.

3. All the parts in it were played by children.

4. The Hunchback of Notre Dame. Several films, based on the novel *Notre Dame of Paris* by Victor Hugo, have been made about the bell ringer of Notre Dame cathedral in Paris, the most famous of which starred Charles Laughton.

5. A fish.

6. The Oscars, or Academy Awards, are awards given annually for outstanding performance and achievement in the cinema. As well as Oscars for Best Film, Best Actress etc. there are also Oscars for

technical achievements such as special effects. The first Oscar was given in 1927, and was so nicknamed because it was thought to resemble an actress's Uncle Oscar!

7. Michael J. Fox in the *Back To The Future* movies.

8. Kylie Minogue.

9. Al Jolson in 1927. These were the first words ever to be spoken in a full-length film and heralded the advent of the 'talkies'.

10. *Dial M For Murder*. Whenever you watch a film directed by Alfred Hitchcock see if you can spot Hitchcock himself – he always gave himself a 'walk-on' part!

11. She dreamt of having *Breakfast At Tiffany's*. Tiffany's is a famous expensive New York jeweller's; the film *Breakfast At Tiffany's* was based on a short novel of the same name by American writer Truman Capote.

12. Marlene Dietrich.

13. (a) 1,000,000 years BC. (This film featured cavemen fighting dinosaurs – in reality all the dinosaurs had died before man evolved!)

14. He could talk to the animals.

15. Jessica Rabbit.

16. She hoped that the Wizard of Oz would be able to send her home, not realizing that the Wizard was, in fact, an elaborate conman.

17. *Casablanca*. It was based on a play called *Everyone Comes to Rick's* (the name of the character played by Bogart in the film).

18. The James Bond Movies are: *Doctor No, From Russia With Love, Goldfinger, Thunderball, You*

*Only Live Twice, On Her Majesty's Secret Service,
Diamonds Are Forever, Live And Let Die, The Man
With the Golden Gun, The Spy Who Loved Me,
Moonraker, For Your Eyes Only, Octopussy, Never
Say Never Again, A View To A Kill, The Living
Daylights, A Licence To Kill* and the 'spoof', *Casino
Royale.*

19. Sleepy, Grumpy, Dopey, Bashful, Happy, Sneezy and
    Doc.

20. The two hecklers from *The Muppet Show* and the
    Muppet movies.

CINEMA CONUMDRUMS / 3 – PAGE 70

1. The Blank was really singer Breathless Mahoney (played by Madonna) in disguise.

2. Annie.

3. She was shot.

4. Paul Hogan.

5. The Jedi in *The Return of the Jedi*.

6. King Arthur. Excalibur was the name of King Arthur's sword.

7. John Travolta who played the part of dancer Tony Manera in both films.

8. A Nightmare.

9. A Baby.

10. A kiss from a handsome prince.

11. Oliver Twist in the musical *Oliver!*

12. David Bowie in the 1976 science fiction film of the same name.

13. A mermaid.

14. (d) *Sophie's Choice. Gandhi* won the Oscar in 1982,

The Godfather in 1972, *Chariots of Fire* in 1981, and *Rain Man* in 1988.

15. In the Little Shop of Horrors.

16. *Batman.*

17. Supergirl. Supergirl's real name is Kara, and when she was on Earth she adopted the name of Linda Lee Danvers.

18. Her dog, Toto, and the Tin Man, the Scarecrow and the Cowardly Lion.

19. (a) *Tootsie*; (b) *Some Like It Hot.*

20. *Victor Victoria.*

1. Luke Skywalker's in the *Star Wars* series of movies.

2. A stolen and priceless jewel.

3. Arnold Schwarzenegger who has starred in *The Terminator, Predator* and *Conan*

4. King Kong.

5. The Pet Shop Boys.

6. The Beatles who travelled in a Yellow Submarine in the cartoon film of the same name made in 1968.

7. He gave her lessons in elocution and deportment to win a bet that he could make Eliza, who was just a common flower seller, into a lady. The film and stage musical of *My Fair Lady* are based on a play, *Pygmalion*, by George Bernard Shaw.

8. (d) *Meet Me In St Louis.*

9. She plays the part of Lois Lane, Superman's girlfriend.

10. Judge Doom.

11. He used his large ears.

12. *Grease.*

13. It could fly. *Chitty Chitty Bang Bang* was based on a book by Ian Fleming – who also wrote the James Bond series of novels!

14. *Psycho.*

15. (b) A

16. Woody Allen in the film *Play It Again Sam* which was about Allen's fascination with the Humphrey Bogart film *Casablanca*. In fact, in *Casablanca* Humphrey Bogart never tells Sam, the piano player to 'Play It Again'. He asks him just to 'Play It'. So the most famous line from *Casablanca* was never spoken at all!

17. Pee-Wee Hermann.

18. The Marx Brothers were Groucho, Harpo, Chico, Gummo and Zeppo.

19. His left foot. He received the award for Best Actor for his performance in the film *My Left Foot.*

20. (a) 'Bright Eyes' – *Watership Down*; (b) 'Over the Rainbow' – *The Wizard of Oz*; (c) 'Summer Loving' – *Grease*; (d) 'Climb Every Mountain' – *The Sound of Music*; (e) 'What I Did For Love' – *A Chorus Line*.

1. It helps the medicine go down, in a most delightful way, according to Mary Poppins, as played by Julie Andrews!

2. In Beverly Hills.

3. (a) A shark; (b) A dog; (c) A dog; (d) A giant ape.

4. Charlie Chaplin. Charlie Chaplin is probably the most famous comedian who ever lived. He was born in poverty in South London in 1889, but soon became famous for his portrayal of a down-on-luck clown with a bowler hat and a walking stick in many short films. He moved to America and directed and acted in some classic comedies like *The Kid*, *Modern Times* and *City Lights*. Charlie was knighted by the Queen towards the end of his life and he died in 1977. A statue of him stands in London's Leicester Square.

5. Michael Crawford.

6. Jane.

7. (a) Judy Garland
   (b) John Wayne
   (c) Marilyn Monroe
   (d) Michael Caine

8. *The Ten Commandments.*

9. (a) Batman – Michael Keaton; (b) Superman – Christopher Reeve; (c) Lex Luthor – Gene Hackman; (d) Dick Tracy – Warren Beatty; (e) The Joker – Jack Nicholson.

10. His monster, in the film *Frankenstein*, which was based on a novel by Mary Shelley. Over the years many actors have played the part of Frankenstein's Monster, including Boris Karloff (the first monster) and Bela Lugosi and Christopher Lee (both of whom are more famous for playing the part of that other classic monster, Count Dracula).

11. The Golden Fleece.

12. St Trinian's.

13. Prince.

14. (a) *South Pacific*; (b) *Funny Girl*; (c) *Annie*; (d) *A Star Is Born* (1976)

15. (a) Katharine Hepburn. The first version of *A Star Is Born* was made in 1937 and starred Janet Gaynor; the second was made in 1954 and featured Judy Garland; and Barbra Streisand's version of the story came out in 1976.

16. Rhett Butler (played by Clark Gable) to Scarlett O'Hara (played by Vivien Leigh) in the 1939 classic *Gone With the Wind*.

17. *The Rocky Horror Picture Show*. The Time Warp is a dance.

18. Doctor Strangelove, played by comedian Peter Sellers. *Doctor Strangelove* is a satire on nuclear war and militarism.

19. Diana Ross. She played the part of tragic jazz and blues singer Billie Holiday.

20. Elliot.

CINEMA CONUNDRUMS / 6 – PAGE 78

1. Momma in *Throw Momma From The Train*.

2. One of the third kind.

3. The Wrath of Khan; Khan was a character who had appeared almost twenty years ago in the original *Star Trek* TV series!

4. *She-Devil*, an adaptation of Faye Weldon's bestselling novel *The Life and Loves of a She-devil*.

5. James Dean. *Rebel Without A Cause* was released after Dean's death in a car accident in 1955 at the age of 24. Even though he only made two other films in his life (*East of Eden* and *Giant*) James Dean is one of the best known and loved actors ever.

6. *Ghostbusters*.

7. Bing Crosby in the movies *Holiday Inn* and *White Christmas*. This song is one of the bestselling and best known popular songs of all time and was written in 1942 by Irving Berlin.

8. Supercalifrajalisticexpiallidocious!

9. Cliff Richard.

10. Basil.

11. HAL.

12. A newspaper reporter and a good friend of Superman's. They met each other as children in the town of Smallville.

13. *Brighton Rock.*

14. *The Grapes of Wrath*, which was based on the novel by John Steinbeck.

15. Marlon Brando.

BOOK BAFFLERS / 1 –
PAGE 83

1. Winnie the Pooh.

2. The Famous Five.

3. 13¾

4. A hobbit (to be more precise, the hobbit Bilbo Baggins).

5. It turned her into Supergran.

6. The Borrowers in the books by Mary Norton.

7. A dead tree which had been struck by lightning. In the Follyfoot books by Monica Dickens it was the custom every morning to throw a bucket of water on the tree – in the hope that it would one day start to leaf again.

8. A teddy bear, namely T. R. Bear in the books by Terrance Dicks. T. R. is short for Theodore Roosevelt. Teddy bears are called thus because one of the first ones was given to Theodore Roosevelt, who was American President from 1901-09: 'Teddy' is the shortened form of Theodore.

9. Pippi Longstocking.

10. At midnight when the clock struck thirteen in *Tom's Midnight Garden*.

11. Alice in *Alice In Wonderland*. This book by Lewis Carroll (the pen-name of clergy man and mathematician Charles Dodgson) was first published in 1865, and its sequel *Through The Looking Glass* in 1872. They quickly became much-loved classics. The character of Alice was supposedly based on that of Alice Liddell, the daughter of one of Dodgson's friends.

12. Fungus.

13. The Snowman in the book by Raymond Briggs.

14. Dorothy Gale was on her way to the Emerald City where she hoped that the Wizard of Oz would show her the means to return to her home in Kansas. Many sequels have been written to *The Wizard of Oz* by Frank L. Baum, such as *Glinda of Oz* and *The Scarecrow of Oz*, and the original book has, of course, also been turned into one of the most popular films of all time.

15. Peter Pan. The play by J. M. Barrie has been an enduring success since it first appeared, and a certain amount of the proceeds received on sales of the book, royalties from the play etc. go to the Great Ormond Street Hospital for children in London.

16. Captain Hook.

17. Sherlock Holmes. (221b Baker Street is a real address, and every year thousands of letters are still received addressed to the great detective! 221b is currently, however, the home of a building society.)

18. The great lion Aslan spoke these words at the coronation of the Pevensie children Peter, Edmund, Susan and Lucy in *The Lion, The Witch and The Wardrobe*.

19. In the *Peanuts* cartoon strip, written and drawn by Charles M. Schulz.

20. For wearing red socks.

WITCHES AND WIZARDS, DUNGEONS AND DRAGONS – PAGE 87

1. Witches.

2. Mary Poppins. She promised to remain until the wind changed direction. The original book, written by P. L. Travers, was followed by many others, and, of course, a Walt Disney film.

3. Gandalf the Grey. Gandalf was also to appear in *The Lord of the Rings*, in which he befriended Bilbo's nephew, Frodo.

4. Diggory Kirke, the young boy in C. S. Lewis's *The Magician's Nephew* who together with Polly Plumber travelled to Narnia on its day of creation. The Magician in question was Diggory's Uncle Andrew.

5. The Wicked Witch in the Snow White story. The mirror's final reply to the Witch was that Snow White was more beautiful than she.

6. Pern.

7. Eustace Clarence Scrubb.

8. The magician was Merlin, and the Wart's more common name was Arthur – he grew up, of course,

to be King Arthur. T. H. White's *The Sword In The Stone* is his own personal version of the legend of King Arthur, and was the basis for a successful Walt Disney cartoon. In history King Arthur most probably existed, but sadly not as a king, but as a chieftain and mighty warrior in sixth-century Britain; there's a possibility too that Merlin existed – but as a Welsh poet, not a mighty magician!

9. Jadis, the White Witch in *The Lion, The Witch, And the Wardrobe*.

10. The three guardian angels who helped Meg and Calvin in Madeleine L'Engle's *A Wrinkle In Time*.

11. Ged, or Sparrowhawk.

12. The gold of the Dwarfs in *The Hobbit*.

NURSERY RHYMES –
PAGE 89

1. Three score and ten.

2. An old man clothed in leather.

3. Pickled pepper.

4. 'The Moon does shine as bright as day'.

5. Lean.

6. In a shoe.

7. 'I'm sure I don't know'.

8. Sugar and spice and all things nice (while little boys are made of frogs and snails and puppy dogs' tails!).

9. A pocketful of posies. (This seemingly innocent nursery rhyme is actually about the bubonic plague of the 1600s! Pinkish spots (or rings of roses) and a sneezing fit were common symptoms of the plague.)

10. The fly with his little eye.

11. A spider.

12. 'With silver bells and cockle shells and pretty maids all in a row.' (The 'Mary Mary quite contrary' in this rhyme is thought by some people to be Mary, Queen of Scots.)

13. Old King Cole.

14. 'The child that is born on the Sabbath day
    (ie. Sunday) is bonny and blithe and good and gay.'

15. The farmer's wife.

16. Jack (Jill 'came tumbling after')

17. The dish.

18. A 'fine lady upon a white horse'.

19. Sixpence ('Sing A Song Of Sixpence')

20. The Lion and the Unicorn.

BOOK BAFFLERS / 2 –
PAGE 92

1. The dropping of a nuclear bomb and the resulting radioactive fallout which eventually killed them.

2. *The Lord of the Rings*. The three books in the series are: *The Fellowship of the Ring*; *The Two Towers*; and *The Return of the King*. They follow on from the events described in Tolkien's other classic, *The Hobbit*.

3. She grew taller. (When she drank from a bottle marked 'Drink Me' she grew shorter.)

4. Baloo was a bear who looked after the wolf-cubs in the forest, and Bagheera was the wise old Black Panther. (Their arch enemy was Shere Khan, the tiger).

5. The Borrowers.

6. The Railway Children. Their adventures are told in the book of the same name by E. Nesbit.

7. The key which led her into a Secret Garden and the people who dwelt there, in the book *The Secret Garden* by Frances Hodgson Burnett.

8. The Walkers and Blacketts.

9. Julian, Dick, Anne, George (Georgina) and Timmy the dog.

10. Pam, Barbara, Colin, Jack, George, Peter and Janet.

11. Robin Hood's band of merry men who lived in Sherwood Forest. They robbed from the rich and gave to the poor and their archenemy was the Sheriff of Nottingham. There's no proof that Robin Hood actually existed; his adventures were first mentioned in the twelfth century.

12. The Little Prince, in the book by Antoine St Exupery.

13. Hitler.

14. Joan Aiken.

15. Sherlock Holmes in the short story *The Final Problem*. However, so great was the public's demand for more Sherlock Holmes stories that his author, Sir Arthur Conan Doyle, was forced to 'resurrect' him and bring him back!

16. Rubadub. These names are all places in which Barney and his friends, Roger, Dinah and Snubby found adventure in the series of books by Enid Blyton.

17. He was eaten by the crocodile which had been pursuing him for years.

18. His friend Chang. Once in Tibet he did indeed find his friend Chang – and the Yeti, or Abominable Snowman! The Yeti is a legendary ape-like creature which is said to live in the Himalayas. No evidence has been produced to prove conclusively that it does or doesn't exist.

19. A collection of dinner plates, discovered by Allie in *The Owl Service* by Alan Garner.

20. The Norwegian coastline.

MYTHS AND LEGENDS –
PAGE 94

1. On Mount Olympus, one of the highest mountains in Greece. It is in the north of that country.

2. Zeus and Hera; their Roman counterparts were Jupiter and Juno.

3. All the troubles of the world, and Hope. (Before Pandora opened her box, the world was supposedly a carefree and happy place.)

4. He was given the power to turn everything he touched into gold. That was very fine until he found that even his food, and people he loved, also turned to gold!

5. The Underworld, or the land of the dead. This land was also known by the name of Hades.

6. War.

7. Asgard was the home of the Norse gods. It was supposedly connected to the Earth by a rainbow bridge. The Norse gods include Odin (or Wotan) the King of the Gods, Thor, the Thunder God and Odin's son, and Loki, the God of Mischief.

8. Aphrodite – she is better known by her Roman name, Venus. According to some legends she was

born from the foam of the sea, and there is a famous painting by the Italian artist Botticelli showing just this event.

9. In the Underworld or land of the dead, where she was married to its king, the God Hades. She would return to Earth every summer. During the cold and bleak winter, when she was living in the Underworld the world was supposedly in mourning for her.

10. The Golden Fleece.

11. Helen of Troy. When Paris, a prince of the city of Troy abducted her from her husband, Menelaus, Menelaus declared war on Troy.

12. They built an enormous wooden horse and left it outside the Gates of Troy. Delighted by this homage to their god, the Greeks opened the gates and brought the horse inside their walled city. But the horse was hollow, and out of it at dead of night came armed Greek warriors who devastated the town. For many years people thought the story of Troy was just a legend. There is no evidence that there ever was a Trojan Horse, but in 1871 a German archaeologist Heinrich Schliemann unearthed the ruins of Troy in north-western Turkey!

13. The Oracle of Delphi.

14. His own reflection in the water. Even today someone who is overly vain is said to be a 'narcissist'.

15. Prometheus. For this crime the gods chained him to a massive rock and sent an eagle to devour his liver. Overnight his wounds would heal until the following day when the eagle would come again!

16. Despite his father's warnings Icarus flew too close to the sun and the sun's heat melted the wax which held his wings together. He fell into the sea and drowned.

17. To Valhalla.

18. He went to the Underworld in search of his lover Eurydice who had died. He finally persuaded the King of the Underworld to allow Eurydice to return to the land of the living – on the condition that he should lead her out and not turn round to look at her until they had reached the surface world. But Orpheus did turn round to sneak a look – and lost Eurydice until he, himself, died and went down to the Underworld.

19. Cerberus.

20. Eros – or Cupid as the Romans called him.

BOOK BAFFLERS / 3 –
PAGE 97

1. *The Dawn Treader.*

2. Rebecca.

3. Because their home burrow was being threatened by human builders.

4. In the dump (in reality a chalk pit) the twentieth-century Stig found a friendly caveman.

5. Aunt Sally in the Worzel Gummidge books by Barbara Euphran Todd.

6. Nigel Molesworth, in the books by Ronald Searle and Geoffrey Willans.

7. St Trinian's.

8. He turned himself into an evil, twisted murderer, Mister Hyde.

9. The breakdown of society ofter the holocaust in the books by Peter Dickinson.

10. Ged, the trainee magician.

11. A deed of property.

12. Some minor trinkets, pistols, tobacco, shells – and a treasure map.

13. A 'midnight garden'.

14. Mary, Queen of Scots. Mary was not of course assassinated in a plot, but was executed in 1587 on the orders of her cousin Queen Elizabeth I who feared that the Roman Catholic Mary posed a threat to her throne. After the death of Elizabeth in 1603 Mary's son James became King of England.

15. They were very small.

16. (a) James; (b) Charlie.

17. *Wuthering Heights.*

18. A horse.

19. The Mad Hatter, the March Hare and the Dormouse.

20. The One Ring, possession of which would give Sauron mastery over all things.

BACK TO THE FUTURE – PAGE 100

1. A venomous thinking and mobile giant plant, in John Wyndham's classic science fiction novel *The Day of the Triffids*.

2. A comet.

3. Small humanoid creatures living on Earth, from the novels by Terry Pratchett.

4. He was whizzed off into space by his alien friend Ford Prefect when the Earth was destroyed to make way for an intergalactic bypass. *The Hitchhiker's Guide to the Galaxy* was originally a BBC radio series which then gave birth to a series of books, and then to a television series!

5. Twenty thousand leagues. A league is an old unit of measurement and is roughly equal to three miles. 'Nemo' is a Latin word meaning 'no-one'.

6. 1984. George Orwell originally wanted to call his novel 1948 (the book was written in that year) until his publisher persuaded him otherwise!). The book has been made into two popular films – one starring Peter Cushing, and the other John Hurt (with music by the Eurythmics).

7. The Space Odyssey took place in the year 2001;

contact was made in the year 2010. These two books by Arthur C. Clarke are, of course, also the basis of two successful science fiction films.

8. Dune in the series of books by Frank Herbert.

9. To the centre of the Earth in the book by Jules Verne.

10. A Capping was a brain implant performed on every male when he came of age and which ensured that he remained docile and obedient to the evil Tripods, aliens from another planet.

11. Beyond the White Mountains in the south were the lands which were free from the rule of the Tripods.

12. The planet Dune.

13. Dinosaurs. The Lost World was supposedly a plateau in Africa, so isolated that dinosaurs had never become extinct. In reality, of course, the dinosaurs became extinct about 65 million years ago, possibly because of a change in the Earth's climate. They were the ruling species on Earth for about 150 million years; by comparison man has been around for only 40,000 years!!

14. (a) the Joker; (b) the Mekon; (c) Ming the Merciless; (d) Lex Luthor.

15. Luke: he was the heir apparent to one of the settlements in an England which had reverted into primitiveness following the great Disaster.

1. Cleopatra in *Antony and Cleopatra*. She killed
   herself upon hearing the news that Antony was dead.
   Antony and Cleopatra are, of course, real historical
   characters and they both died in 30 BC. Mark Antony
   also appears in Shakespeare's other play, *Julius
   Caesar*.

2. *Hamlet*. Elsinore is in Denmark, and to this day the
   play is often performed in the castle there.

3. (a) Romeo – Juliet; (b) Othello – Desdemona;
   (c) Hamlet – Ophelia; (d) Julius Caesar – Calphurnia;
   (e) Antony – Cleopatra; (f) Petruchio – Katherina (in
   The Taming of the Shrew).

4. Goneril, Regan, and Cordelia. Of the three Cordelia
   was the only sister who truly loved her father and
   didn't use him for her own gain.

5. Shylock. He was thwarted when he was told that he
   would lose all his possessions if he took from
   Antonio even one ounce more or less of flesh, or one
   drop of blood.

6. *Macbeth*. Macbeth was an actual King of Scotland
   who reigned from 1040 to 1057. In Shakespeare's
   play he became King by murdering King Duncan in

his bed; in reality he killed Duncan in a fair battle!
(This play has such a reputation for causing bad luck
(possibly because of the presence of the witches in
it) that you will find that most superstitious actors
will not refer to the play by its proper name –
instead they may call it 'The Scottish Play'.)

7. Julius Caesar. The real-life Julius Caesar ruled Rome
from 46 BC until 44 BC when, as in Shakespeare's
play he was assassinated by a group of conspirators
who included Brutus and Cassius.

8. An ass' head.

9. The Montagues (Romeo's family) and the Capulets
(Juliet's family) in *Romeo and Juliet.*

10. The Ides of March is another name for March 15.
Julius Caesar was warned by the soothsayer
Artemidorus to beware this date. He ignored the
advice and was assassinated on that day.

11. They predicted that Macbeth would become Thane
of Glamis, Thane of Cawdor and King of Scotland.

12. Ophelia drowned herself when Hamlet spurned her
love for him.

13. (a) Hamlet
    (b) Othello
    (c) Pericles
    (d) Antonio

14. *The Tempest.*

15. England.

16. (c) *Edward II.* This play was written by Christopher
Marlowe – who some people think wrote some of
Shakespeare's plays!

17. *Hamlet.*

18. Julius Caesar.

19. Polonius, in *Hamlet*, was stabbed while hiding behind an arras – a heavy and ornate curtain . . .

20. (a) *Hamlet*
   (b) *Romeo and Juliet*
   (c) *The Merchant of Venice*
   (d) *Julius Caesar*
   (e) *Twelfth Night*
   (f) *Hamlet*

1. A pony which the children were forced to leave behind on the island Clerinel, when Hitler invaded the Channel Islands in 1940. Their story is told in the book *We Couldn't Leave Dinah* by Mary Treadgold. The Channel Islands were the only part of Great Britain to be invaded by the Germans in the Second World War.

2. The creature (or sand-fairy) discovered by Robert, Anthea, Jane, Cyril and the Baby in *Five Children and It* by E. Nesbit and which had the questionable power of being able to make one's fondest wishes come true.

3. Smith.

4. *A Wrinkle in Time.*

5. He was the Last of the Mohicans, in the book of the same name by James Fennimore Cooper. The Mohicans were a tribe of native North American Indians.

6. Napoleon.

7. Kim.

8. Luke, the heir to a native settlement in an England

turned primitive after the great Disaster, in the books by John Christopher.

9. Count Dracula in the novel by Bram Stoker. Dracula has been played many times in the cinema, but the character was actually based on a thirteenth century Romanian named Vlad Dracul, who was a heartless tyrant but definitely not a vampire!

10. Adrian Mole.

11. *Black Beauty,* the only book written by Anna Sewell. *Black Beauty* is certainly a children's classic, but Sewell actually wrote it to encourage adults to treat their horses in a better way!

12. Elrond, who lived in Rivendell in J. R. R. Tolkien's *The Lord of the Rings.*

13. Greed and selfishness. The three ghosts reminded him of his past, showed him what people thought of him in the present, and how people would react to his death. So shocking to Scrooge were these revelations that he became a reformed character literally overnight.

14. A giant whale. Ahab perished with almost all of his shipmates in pursuit of Moby Dick.

15. The invaders came from Mars. All the weapons of the peoples of Earth were useless against the Martians: but in the end they were killed by a lowly virus against which they had no immunity. (*The War of the Worlds* was written in 1898, but so powerful was the story that when actor Orson Welles read the story on American radio in 1930 people actually believed that the Martians had landed!)

16. They were shipwrecked on a desert island.

17. Buck, a St Bernard dog.

18. 1984.

THE CLASSICS – PAGE 108

1. (a) *A Tale of Two Cities,* by Charles Dickens;
   (b) *Moby Dick*, by Herman Melville; (c) *Alice's
   Adventures Through the Looking Glass,* by Lewis
   Carroll; (d) *Pride and Prejudice* by Jane Austen.

2. Robinson Crusoe, in the book by Daniel Defoe.

3. The Scarlet Pimpernel. Between 1789 and 1795
   France was torn apart by revolution, and the
   aristocrats, who had ruled the country, were in
   danger of losing their lives at the guillotine. The
   Scarlet Pimpernel was an English nobleman who
   smuggled them out of France and to safety. In 1989
   the whole of France celebrated the two hundredth
   anniversary of the Revolution.

4. *I, Claudius*, and *Claudius the God*. Claudius lived
   from 10 BC to 54 AD. He became Emperor of Rome
   in 41 AD, when the Emperor Caligula was murdered;
   Claudius himself was murdered probably by his own
   wife in 54 AD!

5. Bathsheba first married Sergeant Troy and, when he
   died, the farmer Gabriel Oak. *Far From The
   Madding Crowd* is one of Thomas Hardy's most
   popular novels and was also made into a film
   starring actress Julie Christie.

6. *Frankenstein.* The original Prometheus in Greek

myth was the Titan who gave the secret of fire to mankind and thus earned the wrath of the gods.

7. Mr Rochester. At the end of the book Jane Eyre married him.

8. Tiny Tim – *A Christmas Carol;* Miss Haversham – *Great Expectations;* The Artful Dodger – *Oliver Twist;* Peggoty – *David Copperfield;* Little Nell – *The Old Curiosity Shop.*

9. *Brave New World.*

10. Gormenghast. The three books in Mervyn Peake's weird and macabre *Gormenghast* trilogy are *Titus Groan, Gormenghast,* and *Titus Alone.*

11. Allan Quatermain. Rider Haggard wrote many other adventure stories set at the turn of the century, including *Allan Quatermain* and *She,* a tale of a mysterious queen with the secret of eternal life.

12. A gorilla.

13. Nobody knows! *The Mystery of Edwin Drood* by Charles Dickens was a novel about the disappearance and supposed murder of Edwin Drood – but Dickens died before he could finish the book! Many people have advanced theories about who was responsible for Edwin's death – or if, indeed, he did die. The choice is yours!

14. Twenty – three for the Elves, seven for the Dwarfs, nine for Mortal Men, and one for the Dark Lord 'on his dark throne'.